COURAGEOUS COMPANIONS

by CHARLES J. FINGER

pictures by JAMES H. DAUGHERTY

LONGMANS GREEN & Co.

LONGMANS, GREEN AND CO.

55 FIFTH AVENUE, NEW YORK
221 EAST 20TH STREET, CHICAGO
TREMONT TEMPLE, BOSTON
128 UNIVERSITY AVENUE, TORONTO

LONGMANS, GREEN AND CO. LTD.

39 PATERNOSTER ROW, E C 4, LONDON
53 NICOL ROAD, BOMBAY
6 OLD COURT HOUSE STREET, CALCUTTA
167 MOUNT ROAD, MADRAS

FINGER
COURAGEOUS COMPANIONS

FIRST EDITION

PRINTED IN THE UNITED STATES OF AMERICA

Dedicated to

THE MEMBERS OF THE

AMERICAN LIBRARY ASSOCIATION

BECAUSE

THEIR VISION AND HOPE AND RADIANT IDEAL

MAKE LIFE FLOW LIKE A FLASHING RIVER

FOR A YOUNG GENERATION

And better had they ne'er been born,
Who read to doubt, or read to scorn.
— WALTER SCOTT

CONTENTS

ILLUSTRATIONS

COURAGEOUS COMPANIONS

CHAPTER I

The Coming of the Ships

IN THE gray dawn, on a day when men still talked of
Columbus and his voyage, two ships dropped into Portsdown harbor. One of them was well-kept and trim, the
other weather-beaten and ragged of sail. From their decks
nothing could be seen of the village because of a low hill that lay
between it and the sea. Only the castle tower lifted above the
morning mist, so sailors on the weather-beaten ship who had
not been to that port before, thought the bay one without people or town.

Ashore, the first sight of the ships had made something of a stir, for, from the castle tower, young Dick Osberne had seen them while they still looked like thin sea ghosts. So he had called Hugh of the Mill and together they had watched for the best part of an hour. While the lads differed about the stranger ship they were agreed that the well-kept one was Sir Robert's *Seagull*. And the *Seagull* had been away for four weeks, chasing the pirate Kellwanton who had harried the coasts of Wales and Cornwall. Four weeks being a long time for such a chase, the people of Portsdown had wondered.

Some of them were wondering that morning, early though it was, for those were days when men did not stay long abed after light had come. So in the village street the smith and the armorer met, gave one another a good morning, then asked the question they had asked every day for the half of a month, " Now what think ye of the absence of the *Seagull?* " The smith added, " There have been storms, and it would be a sad thing if the ship had been cast away."

The armorer answered, " For me, I would not open an eye in wonder to hear that Sir Robert had sailed his *Seagull* to this new-found America. He is that kind of man. They tell me that he has a map made by a pirate by which he knows all the seas and islands. They say that a Spanish Don gave him a compass needle, one of the best and truest ever made. By such needle, that always points truly north, a good seaman may find his way in the dark over unsailed waters, a thing most wonderful."

" That may be," said the smith. " Still, I hear strange things about the Americas. In Greenland, they tell me, there is a mountain of iron of such strange power that when near it a ship's compass loses its property and no ship with iron can get away, but is drawn to the mountain in spite of wind or oar, which would be a fearful thing, look you. I know something of the lodestone, and do not doubt but that with a mountain of it the very nails might be drawn out and fly from a ship so that the vessel would fall apart."

The armorer made a frown, not in anger but of puzzlement, and said, " I heard Red Head, the pirate from which Sir Robert took Osberne of the castle, I heard him say that near the Americas the lands themselves are not set solid in the sea as England is. Near this same Greenland there stood an island that was utterly consumed by fire. In other islands sailors have been so deceived by demons that they could not go on land, without danger. This Columbus found a place of little worth when he found America. Never will men go there. Who would dwell in such a place, I ask ? "

In answer the smith shook his head, then, not to end the talk, though that part of it was finished, touched on a new field. " I have often wondered about young Osberne that Sir Robert took from the pirate. What history may be behind the lad none can tell."

" Maybe stolen from some great family " said the armorer.

" Or mayhap lost at sea and found by the pirate," guessed the smith, saying something he had said a hundred times and more. " But he is a lad with a happy smile and a quick wit, and of willing readiness. Many's the time he has lent a hand down at the forge."

" A willing hand," added the armorer. " Small wonder that he sees to things at the castle, telling the servants to come and to go, although his years can be no more than sixteen."

" Not a day more," agreed the smith. " I like the way he looks into your eyes when talking. A lad good at wrestling, at his bow and arrow, at his quarterstaff too. He swims well and he runs, beaten only in that by Hugh of the Mill. He is at home in the Spanish tongue as in the English they tell me. And, talk of the devil and you will see his hoof, here he comes now with Sir Robert's horse. What's afoot, I wonder?"

"Any good tidings, Osberne?" shouted the armorer as Osberne passed, and the lad halted for a moment.

"Why so early astir with Sir Robert's horse?" asked the smith.

"The *Seagull* rides in the bay," answered Osberne. "We saw her as she rounded the point, and another ship, a foreign one, is with her."

"The captured pirate, belike," said the armorer.

"I doubt that, for there is no pirate look about her. A pirate would have no ragged sails. I know that all goes well with the *Seagull,* for she flies the arrow flag at her masthead. You had better go and let folk know. Hugh is calling the valley people."

So Osberne went on with the horse. Then the armorer ran into his shop and mounted the ladder to the loft and so came to the roof which overlooked the bay, to see the two ships with his own eyes. He put his hands to his mouth and roared out in bull-like voice, "The *Seagull,* and a stranger! The *Seagull* and a stranger!" And the smith, hearing him from below, betook himself to lusty noise-making, picking up a hammer and beating loudly on a piece of iron that hung by his door, making thereby a great clang and uproar that brought many to their doors. The tailor took up the cry calling, "To the beach! To the beach! The *Seagull* is come!" Next a score and more of boys joined in, and the dogs that followed at their heels helped in the noise-making as dogs will. So the news spread, and people got together and talked of the feast that would be

held, for every good voyage meant feasting and fun and holi-
day, Sir Robert being no stingy voyager to come back with a
ship-load and turn himself into a huckster, trading and bar-
gaining. He was more like to a good householder who comes
from afar with gifts for everybody.

Down to the sea-beach ran the people, old and young, man
and woman, to watch the boat as it came ashore with Sir Robert himself steering it, for he was no man of lazy habit, like so
many of the rich, but one young and active and ready to do
deeds, an adventurer every inch of him. His glittering eyes and
flushed cheek told that. No sooner did the boat's keel scrape
the sand than there were twenty men in the water ready and
willing to lay hands on it and to pull it up so that the boatmen
might step to solid land. And while men were greeting one
another, Will giving a word to John, and Rob holding his oar
in one hand to clasp the fist of Jack, Sir Robert rose, set a foot
on the gunnel, then leaped ashore and waved a greeting, and
shouted a happy word to the villagers. They cheered in welcome, some waving their caps, two blowing trumpets with
more noise than music, the boys and their dogs making louder
fuss than any. Then Sir Robert took the horse from Osberne
and mounted lightly, as a proper horseman should, not holding
on and pulling himself up to the saddle, but setting a toe in
stirrup, his left hand on the mane and his right hand on saddle-
head and gaining his seat with a leap. He went clattering up
to the castle, Osberne running at his stirrup. Some of the
people followed, laughing and shouting, making a long and
straggling line as they went, and the crowd grew because some,
who were too late to get to the beach but were on their way to
it, turned to see what would happen at the gate, though they
knew very well. At the gate Sir Robert halted, then took a

bag that hung at his waist, and, taking out a handful of money, flung it far and wide, whereupon the people scrambled for it much as chickens go after grain, not striving ill-naturedly but in a jolly kind of way. Then Sir Robert rode through the gates to where his household stood in the court-yard. And the lady of the castle, Sir Robert's mother, very fine in rich dress and gold chain, went forward to welcome him, and after proper greetings all passed into the castle.

As for those who stayed down by the sea, they saw what there was to be seen and heard what there was to be heard from the four boatmen. They learned how the *Seagull* had found the pirate Kellwanton attacking the stranger ship, and how Kellwanton had been driven off and beaten until his ship lay on the sea like a wounded duck, and how Kellwanton had been hanged from his own mast, and how Will Long had been put in charge of the pirate ship which was then on its way to Portsdown. While the tale was being told Osberne came down, and with him were two men carrying cloaks and hats and footwear, all of which they put into the boat. Then Osberne with the sailors pulled out to the strange ship and soon after came back with four men whose faces were like the bark of a tree for wrinkles and dark color, and whose hands were like knotted roots for hardness, though their bodies were hidden by the cloaks that Osberne had brought. Yet, as the people saw, when the strangers stepped ashore and the cloaks chanced to flap open, they were dressed in clothes that were mere rags and could hardly hold together, fastened too with thorns in place of buttons or hooks. So everybody was agog for news but only the smith put a question.

"Is it from wars that ye come?" he asked. "Or mayhap you have been to the Americas."

The man to whom he put his question made answer in a rusty kind of English, saying, "To a new America we sailed but the tale must wait, friend. My shipmates are foreign but I am English born and my name is Andrew of Bristol, my work that of a gunner."

So people had to be content with that for the rest of the day because the four went to the castle with Osberne, and there they stayed. Also there was this. Some from the village had to go to work getting ready for the home-coming feast which was to be held on the morrow.

And that feast commenced after the villagers had been to church to give thanks for the return of the *Seagull*. The fun began with a mighty eating, for servants of the castle, and bakers of the village, as well as housewives had been busy at tables and ovens for many an hour. In a smooth place down by the stream long tables were set, and a canopy shaded them from the sun. Down the middle of the tables were jellies of many colors shaped as flowers, trees, animals, fish, fowls and fruits. Like soldiers marching by side of the jellies were gingerbreads, sugarbread, marmalades, conserves of old fruits. There were cheeses of many kinds, and much milk and cream. There were pigs roasted whole, and venison pasties, and custards, and roasted wildfowl, and venison baked, and great rounds of beef, and mutton and veal and bacon and pork and fat capons. Pots of beans and peas and lentils stood here and there. And there were many great loaves of golden-crusted, crisp, white bread. A table set apart for Sir Robert and his household held plates of gold and silver, but the villagers took what they chose and ate it standing. So it was a merry sight with everybody doing his best, and the ladies of the castle in fine dresses of silk, and necklaces of jewels; most of the men too were in their brave finery. But some were in such dress as best suited them for serious business, mainly those who chose to take part in the sports. And everywhere were boys and dogs; shepherd's dogs and mastiffs for the men; little and pretty and proper and fine spaniels for the ladies; boys with prick-eared warners as they were called, being good for nothing but to bark. Also there were musicians with those dogs called dancers, of a kind to do tricks while the music played and while everybody was eating, sometimes standing or walking about on their hind legs dressed in little red coats, or leaping at a sign to snatch a man's hat from his head, or dancing in a clumsy fashion as they had been taught.

A wandering crowd of players had chanced that way and were busy with drum and fife, and the play they played was one that everybody had seen a score of times, called Noah and his wife. It had a great deal of kicking and cuffing and slapping with blown-up bladders; and a merry fellow who played the part of the devil set the people on a roar every time he opened his mouth; and a Noah's wife scolded and pecked; and a Noah, very old and shaky at the knees, who always got into trouble; and a sheriff came and went only to be beaten by everybody. So the play ran on with much noisy music and loud singing until it came to the place where the animals and birds were safely in the ark, but Noah's wife refused to go unless her friends and the devil also went. When it was all ended players and people mixed together, laughing and talking and eating, and some of the villagers put on stage things and capered about, very silly but very happy.

Also there were dancers and tumblers and jugglers. Then there was the sport of grinning through a horse collar with a prize to the lad who could make a face to set most to laughing.

And a small pig was well greased, then set loose, a purse of money for him who could catch and hold it; so there came about a great amount of running and shouting and squealing and falling, but in the end the dogs took part, minded to play the game for themselves, and that meant much calling and whistling and many threats, until the pig found the comfort of his sty and grunted his scorn for the folly of men. Last there were gipsies telling fortunes, and giving advice and filling wives with a fear that some of them would find ways to enter houses and steal spoons and pewter.

So no merrier corner could be found in all England when the trumpet sounded at a sign from Sir Robert, at which the smith, a man liked by everybody, stood on a table and roared out that the sports would begin. He began to make a long talk of it, being one who liked the sound of his own voice, and would have gone on and on, but those crowding round pressed on the table so that it fell, whereupon the smith vanished in the middle of his speech. Away then they all trooped, talking and laughing, the men slapping one another on the back in hearty fashion, girls and boys going hand in hand, matrons nodding their heads in talk, but with few listening.

First there came horse-racing with the stout Devonshire ponies putting spirit into the work, the riders not using saddles but sitting easily bareback. Next there was wrestling on horseback, many a lad getting a good tumble and a hard knock, but taking all with a grin. Then there was quarterstaff play, those in the game wearing a piece of hide to shield themselves somewhat, but for the most part using their staves to ward off blows which were not given lightly.

In the archery contest and the shooting at a target, no less than twelve upright lads joined in. Although somewhat of a

summer breeze had sprung up yet so well did they judge distances and the set of the air that most of them hit the inner
mark and many the bull's-eye. So a closer test was made with
a target no larger than a man's hand hung on a swaying twig,
and three of the lads, Osberne among them, came out with
honor, not missing in five shots. Then those three had to prove
themselves, making their own tests. So Hugh, the miller's
lad, took a piece of board the size of a plate and having set
it up at head height, paced off fifty steps. At that distance he
stuck three arrows in the ground then stood awhile, looking
intently. Next, before a man could count five, and at a time
when the wind had dropped, he shot the arrows, fitting them
to the bow-string with great swiftness, and, lo! and behold,
the three arrows were fixed in the little round board, one in the
center, the second above and almost at the edge, the third
below, and at the edge, and in a straight line with the others.
Then what a shout went up, and how Osberne stepped forth
and shook him by the hand, and how Curtis the armorer's lad
threw up his cap and danced with joy to see the marksmanship!
It came to the turn of Curtis who also took three arrows. But
instead of pacing a course he turned about on his left heel and
drew a circle in the grass with his right, but not a very large
one. After waiting a little until the air was quite still, he shot,
sending the second and third arrow up before the first had
turned in the air, and catching each with a sudden hand sweep
much as a man catches a fly, all without stepping out of the circle
he had made. So the herald lifted a shield, as he had also
lifted it when Hugh shot, to signify that the one trick was as
good as the other, seeing which the people fell to cheering, and
to shaking one another's hands, for the lads were well liked.
Then came Osberne's turn and this is what he did. Taking,

as the others had done, three arrows, he set up three marks, each fifty paces from the place where he had stood, and the targets in a triangle. Then whirling on his heel he let fly his shafts as he turned with quickness, sending an arrow at each turn, three turns and three arrows, with every one going true to its mark. So again the herald lifted his shield to signify that each lad had done as well as his fellow.

" So well and finely was all done," said the knight, " that it was a joy to see. And now for the gift, which is this. Each lad shall have that which he desires for his life's work. If Hugh would be a miller, then a mill he shall have. If Curtis would be an armorer in Exeter town, then a shop shall be his. Osberne too must choose. But not in any hurry. Choose well, for a choice is brief but endless."

Then he gave each of the lads a sword and sheath, the sheath of good brown leather bound with silver grips, and the strings of white silk, telling them that the friendship between them should be a friendship with a sword, each to draw in defense of the good name of the other. And the lads stood before him, their heads bent a little because their hearts were happy and full.

The knight was a little serious when he spoke again saying, " Look well to it, lads, that wherever ye be ye carry yourselves as courageous companions. It cannot be that the three stay together. It is not that way in life. One goes one way, another goes another way. But there are men in this world who do great things, and with them some of ye may meet. Be courageous companions always. Be strength-giving. Set up a habit of good humor and fair dealing. Mix not in plans and intrigues. Wherever ye go, wherever ye be, be courageous companions with other men. Forgive, and welcome, and share. Be not cruel nor indifferent. Bear yourselves like men."

For a while after that the people played, some of them dancing to music, some chatting as they sat on the grass, some
gathered about the men from the strange ship, for they too
were at the feast as well as the sailors of the *Seagull*. And while
all that was going on some went to work setting up a low
platform for the wrestling match, without which in Devon-

shire no fair or merrymaking could be complete. To that all
looked, because out of Cornwall had come a giant of a fellow
who had met all comers and defeated them. Other Cornishmen were with him, his friends and supporters, and they went
about blowing horns and crying out, "The Black Giant of
Truro! The Black Giant of Truro! Bring out your men!
Bring out your men!"

Tall and stark the Cornish champion stood, head above any

man there, a bundle of muscle and bone. That he was strong none could doubt, by the very look of him. There were proofs of his strength too. For while he walked about with his horn-blowing friends they came to a place where twelve men, six on a side, were playing at tug-of-war, the game going very evenly. He stopped to look at them until the struggle ended, then, not without boastfulness, said that twelve men altogether could not pull against him. Thereupon he took the ship's rope and held one end of it in his left hand with part of it wrapped about his waist, and laid hold of an oak sapling with his right arm, and though the twelve pulled and tugged until the sapling bent, they had to give up after a while. The giant could not be torn loose from his hold.

Men of lesser strength and inches wrestled that day, giving and taking, all in good humor, but though the herald called yet none came to tackle the giant as he stood on the platform and challenged boastfully, "Ten score and ten men I have downed! Mayhap two of you will try at a time. One Cornishman is equal to two men of Devon." Then he picked up one of his hornblowers by the belt and lifted him high above his head by way of showing his strength, while the others kept up their cry of "The Black Giant of Truro! The Black Giant of Truro! Bring out your men! Bring out your men!"

"Now this is a grievous thing," said Will the smith to Andrew of Bristol, the sailor from the stranger ship, "I shall get my ribs cracked for my pains but I am minded to tackle this fellow for his very boastfulness."

Andrew of Bristol answered, "I know nothing about wrestling tricks, but I have pulled at many a ship's rope until my muscles are every bit as hard as the giant's. There have been storms, days and days on end, in which none of us dared quit, and it may be if I think of this fellow as a sea storm, or as one of those waves that tear masts out of a ship and yet fail to carry us overboard, then I shall hold out. And it grieves me sore to hear the fellow bragging."

"The danger is the trick that he may know," said the smith. "There lies the danger more than in his strength. But bullying is smoke, courage fire, as the saying goes."

Andrew of Bristol knit his brows and thought for a while. "There are tricks of the sea too," he said. "Those tricks are dangers, yet we face them because we needs must." He pulled off some of his clothes as he spoke and threw them on the ground, then stood naked to the waist and bare-footed. "This is my war gear at times when I fight the sea," he said. Then he stepped to the platform and climbed on it and so stood beside the Black Giant of Truro, looking like a boy beside a grown man because of the difference in size. But those who looked at the sailor closely, seeing something as well as size, beheld a square man with knotted muscles, with a skin tanned golden-brown; well shaped too, tough in arms and legs, quick and steady of eye. Yet he seemed confused in the manner of one not given to stand before a crowd of men. As for the Black Giant, who also was stripped, he stood sound and whole, much better looking than when dressed. So men came crowding to see, a few women too, and most of them foretold broken limbs for the sailor, though they said that to one another, and not openly for the Cornishmen to hear.

"Are you prepared for what may befall?" called the herald.

"The fortune of war," said the sailor. The Giant of Truro only laughed.

" Then to it, and may the stoutest heart win," spoke the
herald.

At once the giant made a rush, trying to catch the sailor in
his grip, but Andrew was like a cat, not seeming to move in a
hurry but nevertheless neatly getting out of the way. Then the
giant reached out and caught his hand at the back of Andrew's
neck with a slap that could be heard over the meadow, but
the sailor was not to be drawn into the giant's clasp that way.
He seemed to bend and thus escape, and no one could tell how
it came about that a moment later he had the giant in his grip
in such a fashion that the Cornishman's left arm was tightly
pinned to his body and Andrew's arms were about his middle,
while, with his right hand, the giant tried to break the hold.
Thus locked together they swayed about the platform, the
sailor now and then lifting the giant, but not able to throw him.
All the while shouts went up from the onlookers, some of them
giving the sailor advice that he could not hear and which would
not avail for victory did he hear. Then, by some strange trick,
the giant flung himself down so as to fall upon Andrew, which
had he done must have crushed the breath out of the sailor because of sheer weight. But the quickness of a lizard was in
the sailor who loosed his hold yet did not quite clear himself,
so that it came about in a way nobody saw that the giant
crouched over the sailor, pinning each of his wrists to the
ground. Thus matters stood for a full minute, and slowly the
giant wrought, bending the sailor's arms until it seemed as if
the man's bones must crack. And next there was the giant
holding the sailor high as the hornblower had been held,
holding and swaying back and forth a little. As a man may
hurl a log, so the giant hurled the sailor out over the heads of
the people. For a moment those who looked saw him in the

air, then he was gone, crashing into a place where the people made way for their own safety's sake.

But Andrew of Bristol, who had been often flung aside by waves mightier than ten giants of Truro, was on his feet and onto the platform in a trice.

"Ho! Little man," laughed the giant, but his laugh was cut short and he gave a grunt as the sailor launched himself at him, wound a leg about his leg, then flung up an elbow that caught the Truro man under the jaw, and tripped him. Down went the giant, but he picked himself up in a mighty rage. Then followed a strange dance, with the sailor dodging and the giant reaching out his long arms to come to grips, and every now and then the sailor dashing in, cool-headed, to fasten himself on the giant and nip him until he groaned. Sometimes the two of them were on the floor, rolling about, snorting and blowing, but for all the giant's weight he could not hold the sailor, who wriggled out of danger like an eel. And when the giant found his feet, then the sailor came leaping at him, gripping so that the Truro man's ribs cracked, and having done his mischief Andrew leaped lightly aside. So presently the people found things going easier, and they laughed a little, freeing themselves from their fear. But one of the foreign sailors being of no mind to let the affair go on and the pluckiest win, and thinking that the odds in size and weight were unfair, also having been a fellow-voyager of the sailor and having his own notions of helping a comrade, drew a knife from his girdle and climbed into the fighting place. Andrew, seeing that, turned on the Spaniard and caught him a clip under the point of the chin that sent him reeling. When the Spaniard regained his feet, which he did soon, the giant, losing his temper at the interference, caught the fellow in a grip that made him yell aloud, whereupon Andrew, now taking the part of his fellow-voyager, swept round swift as lightning, drove with his fist full at the breast of the Truro man in a way and with a force that sent him staggering across the stage. So there was an end of the wrestle that was no proper end at all, and the herald made announcement to that effect.

But Sir Robert had to have a say about the business.

"Sailor," he said, "it was no fair win, from no fault of thine, but it was all well enough done. Thou art no wrestler when it comes to tricks, but a sound and proper man to meet what comes, and it was good to stand forth as champion at a pinch when no other stood forth. So I give this promise, as I made a promise to the archers. If there comes a time when you need a thing done, then count it done by asking my help. In token there is this ring for you to wear. Send it by messenger, or bring it to me or to my friends and what can be done shall be done. A man of might must not be hampered by little wants from the doing of great deeds."

"Fair master," answered the sailor as soon as he could find his voice, for a lump was in his throat at all that praise, he having done more daring deeds with no man looking on, "thanks for the gift. There seems, somehow, to be little that I want. On land I use Shanks' pony. My home is the sea. Of all things in life the best is a good companion, and that no man can provide."

He seemed to be about to say more, but broke down. Indeed that much was said haltingly, almost in the manner of a man ashamed to be talking. Then he went away to find his Spanish companion who had drawn the knife, to explain to him how fights were fought with no thought of ill-feeling, and while they were talking the giant came up, no ill-will being in him for all that he was a boaster. So the three shook hands like good companions and every one was well pleased. Also there is this. Those who wondered at the friendship of Andrew with the man who had drawn the dagger, ceased to wonder that evening when the sailor told his tale, not in a long and straight story, but by odds and ends when several sat together at the inn in the long twilight.

When questioned he seemed to set his chin more firmly. At first the sailor would hardly talk. He was one of those who like to listen and to think. But the smith and the armorer and the tailor and the weaver were all agog for news and of no mood to let a good tale pass, for it was known that the strange ship would leave, wind and tide serving, the next morning, for Amsterdam.

"You met the *Seagull* at sea, did you?" asked the weaver, of the sailor, and the sailor nodded with a little frown.

"As men meet on the highroad, one saluting another," put in the smith, helping the weaver.

"More as a man attacked by robbers might be rescued was the way of it," said the sailor. "We were sailing slow, because of barnacles on the ship's bottom, for we had been out many months, and this pirate, the one your lord hunted, on seeing our plight would have robbed us. Already he was getting the wind of us, preparing to attack, when the *Seagull* came up, and, seeing how matters stood, took the sea-robber in hand. He had no more chance than does a mouse with a cat."

"You said you had been long at sea, friend." It was the smith talking.

"Nigh upon two years," answered the sailor. "In strange seas. In places where ships had never sailed." Then he set-

tled back as if that was all there could be to it, so, for a time
no one said anything.

The silence was broken by the armorer who said that Columbus had made the greatest voyage man had ever made, and
that saying woke the sailor to speech.

"Columbus did a brave thing and great," he said, "but when
it comes to distances, there are greater things to do. Here is
the round world and some day a man must sail away west
until he comes back to the place of beginning. That very thing
I am going to do, and the gift your lord has offered me
shall be the way to go, though how that way may be I do
not know."

"But what of falling off the world?" said the miller. "On
the lower side how shall man or ship hold on? That is what
I want to know."

"Can you fall off to the sky?" asked the sailor. "Or could
you fall off in the night? Yet in the night you are, as might
be said, upside down."

"I never thought of it that way," said the miller.

"There are those who have been eastward round the world
to the Spice Islands and they fell not off, yet that is near being
halfway round. I say that there is a way to the west for that
way I have seen, and my shipmates have seen," said the sailor,
quite simply. "It would be a great adventure to sail through
that passage and beyond, going on and on until the Spice
Islands were seen. That very thing I would venture, given
good companions of my own tongue and land. But failing
them I would go with a Spaniard or a man of Portugal, or
a German."

"But an Englishman for bravery," said the weaver.

"Not so," said the sailor sharply. "Good and bad, brave and

poltroon, fair and false are of all lands. Are there not thieves and palliards and highwaymen in England as elsewhere? Such talk is the talk of one who has seen nothing and been nowhere. Wherefore, in heaven's name, should the English be the bravest? I have seen brave deeds done and could tell them too, by others than our own English."

"Your ship now. Tell us of that. Who owns it and why did it set forth?" asked the smith who was one of those men who could put a question in a pleasing way, not so much because of the words, as by the way he said things.

"There is a merchant of great riches by name of De Haro," answered the sailor. "He fitted a ship and sent it abroad and the captain's orders were to do as he pleased, looking for new lands, seeing how far this America reached to the south. We were to see what riches there were, what fine woods."

"And your ship is full of riches, then," said the armorer, at which the sailor laughed softly.

"Why, as to that," Andrew answered, "had the pirate taken us he would have had a fine prize of stones from the sea-beach. For we loaded them in the Americas into our hold for ballast. No. We got no riches.

"But what of new lands found?" asked Osberne.

"That's the true question," said the sailor. "We touched the Brazils and it was a place of such great beauty, and so rich in fruit and fish, and so kindly a people living there that our pilot went ashore and did not return. After that we sailed south and came to a land of flowers, most beautiful."

"But what of animals and of people?" asked the armorer. "Do men there eat men as has been said?"

"What they eat I cannot say," answered the sailor. "But when you come to look at matters with a clear mind, you may see that few people would eat men, though it is true that the tale runs that men-eaters are everywhere. But think. Man would be a hard kind of food to come at. A man-eater would have to fight for every meal. And why men should eat men in a land where there are fish and fruit and game to be had for the picking up, I could never see."

"Now that has a true ring," said the armorer.

"They were people of gentleness everywhere who took us and fed us when we had no food. They tended us when we were sick with the fever. They brought water to us when we thirsted, not in one place but in many a place. The world is full of good folk and kindly if you will but meet them with a fair face and in a fair way."

"So said Columbus, I have heard," put in the smith. "Belike they were the same people that Columbus saw, and seeing you, remembered him."

"Not so," went on Andrew. "This, you must know was in the far south where Columbus never went. It was so far that the very stars were new. It is a place where the North Star is no longer to be seen. Instead a cross hangs in the sky, a cross of stars."

"And the world warmer the more south you go," said the weaver. "I myself saw the difference coming from Scotland to this place. There was winter. Here is summer. And in France, they say, as you go south it grows steadily more warm."

"No. Warmer to a certain point where you cross the middle of the world," said Andrew, "then colder and colder. It is a windy world and a cold sea, and we sailed south until we came to ice and were near frozen, and in the sea we saw a new kind of sea-elephant, dreadful to look at, with tusks the length of a man's arm. Into that sea I fell one stormy night, and was saved by the very Spaniard who drew the knife at the wrestling to save me, as you saw. A faithful friend, he. That same storm drove us to put about to the northeast, and presently we came to a thousand islands in the middle of the ocean, some small and some large, but with no people on them. We called them Della Pulzella, naming them for the Mother of Christ. Then we went west again to the Americas and found a land we called Terra Sancta Cruz, meaning the land of the Holy Cross, because there we saw this cross of stars set in the sky."

The sailor sat silent for a little while, then took a stick and made lines on the ground, showing how the islands and the new land were, making it clear by saying, " This stone must be taken to be the Islands Della Pulzella." And again, " This line must be the coast of Terra Sancta Cruz." Then he drew a long and crooked line and after moving the point of his stick, saying, " Thus we sailed, following the coast along where before we had been storm-driven and saw little because of the trouble we had. But we came to here, as it may be, and so found an opening into the land. Into that we went; and over here, as it might be, we found more islands, and beyond them a mighty open sea. What lieth beyond no man knows."

" But what think ye, sailor man?" asked Hugh.

" As to that it follows that if a ship should sail, on and on to the west, it must come to the Spice Islands. And that I would see. I would go with any captain minded to make the trial."

" A brave venture," said Hugh. " But I would not have the mind for it. A man with a mill might well stand and starve in such a land."

" Belikes, if you stay here with us, some day Sir Robert may

be persuaded to fit out a ship to sail those seas," said Osberne.
" Or if you must go with your ship, then you may come back."

"I may come back, or I may go wherever I hear that a
ship will be fitted up to make this voyage.   But there are things
I must do.   I have drawn out how these coasts run and remember more.   The captain's friend knows a man of great
merit, near Antwerp, or in a place called Nuremberg.   This
man is to make a copper ball to stand for the world, and on it
he will mark all the known lands, he being gifted to do that.
I, of all my shipmates, noted down how places are, and the
lay of the land."

" A pretty toy for some rich man," said the smith.

" Not that," said the sailor.   " With such a ball hung in a
cabin a captain may see the way to go and measure his distance; he may know where his ship is.   So I shall tell him
about this canal we have found and that too may be set down.
Besides, I have long wished to see the Germanies and other
lands, and a sailor sees little.   A port's a port and the folk in
one are much like the folk in another."

His tale stopped there and they all sat silent listening to the
chirping of evening birds, and hearing faintly the music in the
castle, or giving an ear to the song of the nightingale.   The air
was fragrant with the perfume of flowers, and from the sea
came a light and cool breeze.   Because of all that the men were
not overwilling to part for the night.   But from one house
and another came the voices of women calling to the men and
chiding them for staying out late, and here and there a candle
light in a window blinked out.   So one and another got up and
said " Good-night," some going off, but more staying to say
again and again that it was time to be going.   And some, having gone, called back, their voices softened by distance, so that

good-nights came from many directions. At last there was nothing but the sound of frogs, and of chirping birds; and only the smith, and the sailor, and Osberne remained.

Presently the lad spoke, but softly and as one half fearing to be chidden for asking too much. "Sailor-man," said he, "one thing I ask, if it be not too much. When you find a ship and a way to make this voyage about the world, will you let me know? Will you let me go? If it be but the lowest of tasks I will do them gladly. But fain would I go."

"Lad, 'tis a hard life and a rough," said the sailor.

"That, sailor, I know," answered Osberne. "But this life in the castle is a selfish one and a soft. It seems to me that we are in the world to do things, not to eat and to drink and to stay in one place. Besides . . ." he said, then stopped.

"Go on," said the sailor.

"To do and to dare, that seems worth while. But there is that friendship with a sword, of which Sir Robert spoke. To have a friend for whom one might lay down his life. That, I think, might be known by trial, but never by leading a life of ease. . . I want to see where places are. . . I want to do. . . I want to know true fellowship. . . I trust these words of mine seem not untrue."

"Lad," said the sailor. "Here's my hand on it. Do I go, then you shall have the chance. And go I will and must."

And, as it fell out, the chance that Osberne wanted came to pass. For some six months after the strange ship had sailed away, there came to Portsdown a stranger from London town who stayed overnight at the inn. So Sir Robert, and a friend or two with him went to hear the news, and the stranger told them of many things; of the health of the king; of hard times that were; of the great fight on what was called the Evil May-day when the prentices rose up and tried to take the town. He told also of "a strange growing hate in London against all men of foreign birth," and said that there were then more foreigners in London than ever before in the memory of man.

"Why is that?" asked Sir Robert.

"A great buying of things, so my cousin told me," answered the traveler. "There are Spaniards going about who buy little bells of a kind that have been sent to Russia for trade, and which the Russians, I am told, hang about the necks and collars of their horses, for in that land their carriages have no wheels but run on ice, so the tinkle of the bells pleases them. These they buy by the hundred."

"But the Spaniards have no ice to speak of," said Sir Robert. "Therefore I wonder why they would want the bells."

"I know not," answered the man from London. "But there they are buying the little bells, giving good money for them, too. Not only that, but there is a trade for red caps, and for brass bracelets, and for small mirrors, and for beads of glass. A merchant, a friend of my cousin, by name Kent, told me that within two weeks the buying would be done and then they would seek out a ship to take the things to Spain."

Hearing that Sir Robert's eye flashed.

He said, "And here I am with my ship the *Seagull,* and it idle. Why, look you, I shall go to London. It would be good to get a cargo for Spain, I shall sell what we have, and I have promised Osberne a voyage. Why, all fits together with a click like a door-lock. I shall sail for London, taking what tallow and hides and wool we have here, and good fortune may bring about everything else."

That was why Sir Robert sailed out of Portsdown one fine day in April, and the happiest one on board the little ship was Osberne, who went as a sailor hand.

CHAPTER II

The Sailing of the Fleet

NOW SIR ROBERT sold his cargo for a good price, and when he had his ship cleared a piece of good fortune came to him. For King Harry at his court heard of the knight, of how he had chased pirates, of how he had kept the countryside free from highwaymen and robbers, and the tales did not lose with the telling, so the king must needs see and talk with the Devonshire Sir Robert. Therefore one fine day the knight went to court taking Osberne as his page, and the king asked them many questions. When the tale was done the king swore that such doings deserved reward, so promised many things; but, in the manner of kings, he soon forgot, and there was an end of that matter. But the story of how Sir Robert had been with the king flew far and wide, therefore merchants and shippers began to speak well of the knight and so it came about that when the Spaniards were ready to load the stores they had bought it was no hard matter for the knight to get in touch with them and hire his ship to them. Things went all the easier too because Osberne spoke Spanish with ease. As for Osberne, he was all atingle to go to Spain and, after that, to go with the fleet that would sail from there, and he told the knight of his desire.

"I ask your leave," he said to the knight. "On the day of the fair you promised me a gift, and this is the favor I ask."

For a little time the knight made no answer, then he said, "It is fair enough, lad. Time will come when much of our good blood shall go to these new-found Americas and I do not doubt but that strong nations may grow up there some day. So I give you freedom with a right good will knowing that in those far countries and among strange men you will play a straight game." Then he drew himself up in his masterly way, and said, in a new voice, "Now fall to at once. Look to the loading of the ship, giving a hand here and a hand there. There are new men on board and they must know that things are to be done in no careless way."

So presently there was a great activity with loading the *Seagull* at the Pool, and many strange things went into the hold. There were, besides the bells and the other things for trade and barter, cables and hawsers and ropes of hemp. Once Osberne had to go to Ludgate and show a man with a cart the way to the Pool, and the cart was loaded with medicine, and unguents, and salves, and salt, and a brass pestle and mortar, so the lad dreamed dreams of great fights when all those should be needed for the wounded. Other carts held sacks of beans, and of lentils; and mess-bowls to the number of a hundred, and twice that number of porringers; and choppers, and platters of wood, and cooking pots, and copper things for the kitchen; seeing all of which Osberne thought that an army was to be fed. After all those were put away in the hold they loaded away fifty kegs of gunpowder, each of them a hundred pounds of weight. There were also shot and cannon balls, and lead for the making of bullets, and molds for making of cannon balls. Hard upon that came carts with culverins, falconets and bombards, with a masterly man who talked loud, and who scolded and sometimes threatened when the fellows loading and unloading were heavy-handed with the weapons or careless. Did a man go slow, or stop to look, or spit on his hands, then, " No tarrying here! " the caretaker with the guns would cry. " You would do well to put your back into it." And the caretaker of the guns himself seemed to care nothing for the ship or for the other men. His guns and the like only had interest for him. But Osberne knew him for Andrew of Bristol, the same who had been to Portsdown, and who had tackled the giant. So he drew near, then slapped Andrew on the back and said, " By all the saints, have you forgotten me? "

"Faith," answered Andrew, mighty glad, " It is the lad of the arrow shooting who wants to know fellowship; him and no other. And here's our merry meeting. And these are being loaded to go round the world as I said men would some day. Well, my son," he went on, taking Osberne's hand, " here is the chance for you."

"And do you go on this great voyage from Spain?" asked Osberne. "Is that your mind?"

Andrew pulled his beard, as was his habit, and laughed softly. "Lad, I would go if I had to hide in the hold among the garlic. I would go if I had to starve to skin and bone. I would go if I had to eat rats to live. I would even go if I knew I should die halfway there, for it is well to set a face to a duty a man enjoys. I would girdle the world, and shall, if my strength backs my will."

"That makes my heart glad," said Osberne. "And I, for my part, would gladly be under the banner you follow. Would that I might be the first to go round the world. I shall watch for the place and swim ashore to be first. I shall stand at the fore part of the ship and be first by a boat's length. Some man must be first and why not I?"

MANY A time when, because of one hardship and another, it was good to look back, Osberne tried to call to mind the voyage between London and the Port of Seville in Spain, but the memory of it seemed to have vanished. There were neither storms nor pirates nor head winds, so every one on the *Seagull* was merry enough and there were days and nights when the ship sailed over the Biscay Bay heaving gently on a sunlit sea, looking after herself as the sailors said. So the men told tales, and they sang, and they planned, as sailors will do. There was one Spanish lad, Juan de Zubista, who knew a little of new things afoot in Spain, and many listened to him. Osberne, having known Spanish all his life, as has been said, turned into English what Juan said for those who did not understand.

Juan told the tale of the man who would be master of the fleet, one by the name of Ferdinand Magellan, how he had been a soldier in India for the Portuguese, how he had been in the Moorish wars where some said he had played the traitor and sold food to the enemy, how some in Spain thought that he would again play betrayer and sell the ships to a native king.

When it came to that, Andrew, who had been carving a box, for he was one of those whose hands were never idle, wanted more of it. "What of this native king?" he asked.

"I only know what men say," answered Juan. "It is a tale of how one named Serrao once ran off with a ship of which he was captain. The ship was wrecked. This Captain Serrao then took a pirate junk by trickery and sailed to the unknown lands where he married a princess and so set up for a prince. They say that he wrote a letter to Magellan and in answer Magellan said that he would be with him, if not by way of Portugal then by way of Spain. And now a kinsman of this same Serrao is one of Magellan's captains, and that people do not like."

One of the sailors, a hearty fellow named Hans, said, "I have been to sea many a time, and it is rare that a ship sails without stories being told of the villainies of the captain. It is no new thing."

"A true word," said Andrew.

"Give them their first meal and the grumbling begins," said Hans.

"A bagpipe never says a word until its belly is full, as the saying goes," added Andrew.

"The wonder is how this Serrao came to know of the unknown lands in the far East," said Hans. "There would be the Moors and the things they sold, for they knew of far-away lands. But it maybe that some one went there and came back, much as we went south in our ship and came back."

"There was such a man," said Osberne. " Juan has told me the tale."

So he went on to tell how, when the Portuguese had gone with the first voyagers around Africa and to India, out of the Jungle came a white man, wild-looking and half-naked. He came running, and Moors ran after him to catch him, but he gained the fort first. That night he told the Portuguese a strange tale of wandering: how he had left Italy and walked to Egypt, how he had gone to Mecca, how he had adventured by ship to Persia, how he had gone to India, then sailed with traders from China to new lands of great richness very far to the east. After many years he had turned his face homeward, and found white men once more. Also he had warned the men from Europe that the Moors had a fleet gathered to attack them, whereupon they had made ready and a great sea-battle was fought in which so many thousand Moors were slain that the bodies were heaped on the seashore.

"This man's name. Do you know? " asked Hans.

"Barthema, it was," answered Osberne.

"The same," said Andrew, "I have heard the tale before, but in patches only."

"It seems," went on Osberne, "that when he told his adventures on the ships, there in the India seas, both Magellan and Serrao heard. So Serrao turned traitor to his country Portugal, and went to the lands of riches where he set up as king and somehow sent a letter to his friend Magellan. Then Magellan, as was said, wrote back saying that some day he would be with him, if not by Portugal, then by Spain. He meant, perhaps, that if the Portuguese king would not give him ships and men, then he would put his case before Spain. And put his case he did. But the money for the fleet is being given by merchants and mostly by one named De Haro."

"De Haro, indeed!" exclaimed Andrew. "Then all fits together. I know the name. It was that same De Haro who fitted out the ship in which Hans and I and others went to the Americas when we found this passage leading through the land to a great sea to the west. So, it may be, that De Haro is at the bottom of all this. A man with an eye to trade he is, as I well know."

He thought a minute or two, then brought his fist down on the hatch.

"I see it all," he said. "It is this way. De Haro came to know of these rich lands to the east, the Spiceries they are called. But lands to the east are said to belong to Portugal. Now De Haro fell out with the King of Portugal and went to Spain. He also sent out the ship in which we sailed, to spy out the Americas, and we found a passage through the land and to the west, though we did not follow on as we should have done but could not do, our ships being foul and old, and our sails torn and rotten. So we turned back. Then this friend of the captain who went with us saw that I had marked out on parchment a map of the lands. That is why he took me to Germany after we left Portsdown. In Germany I talked with the map maker and another, a half-mad man of great wisdom, and the two of them looked at my maps and made out of them a globe, cutting on a copper ball a map of the world. I saw it myself."

"It all fits together with a click," said Hans.

"I begin to see," put in Osberne. "Lands westward of a certain line belong to Spain, and to the east to Portugal."

"You have it," said Andrew. "De Haro has fallen out with the King of Portugal and is in favor with the King of Spain, so he would find a way in Spanish seas to the Spiceries, by the west. This fleet is to go the way we went, but far beyond, across the unknown ocean, and until it gets to the Spiceries. And by the globe these men have made, the fleet is to find its way. An adventure it will be, by all the saints! Which of us will be the first man to get round the world?"

"I doubt about being the first man," said Osberne, "for Juan here tells me of one who has already been half round, and if he makes the other half, then he must be the first man."

"How can that be?" asked Hans.

"Listen," said Osberne. "Juan tells me that Magellan bought a slave-boy in the Indies, one named Enrique. This Enrique came from a land far to the east, being taken by the slave-traders from his home. Now suppose that home-land to be the Spiceries. Well enough. Mark this. Magellan took this slave to Spain and there he is now. If Magellan takes the slave with him when he sails westward, and if in time the ships touch the home-land of this Enrique, then it must follow that after all the slave shall be the first man to go round the world."

"That is so," said Hans. "We shall not have gone round until we again touch England. Magellan shall not have gone round when he touches the Spiceries. So the lowliest shall be the greatest among us."

"A slave the first man to go round the world," said Andrew, laughing. "It is strange enough. So there die my hopes."

"And mine," said Hans.

That talk stood out in the mind of Osberne.

So at last they came to the river Guadalquivir and the Port of Seville and for a day Osberne walked about full of wonder, as he had walked about the streets of London. The grand Cathedral of St. Peter's, the Moorish Alcazar, the great University, the courts and fountains and gardens, the flower walk called Las Delicias that ran along the river, the narrow streets and crowded houses in the place called Triana where gipsies and poor people lived; all these held him. He saw, and talked with a man who had sailed with Columbus to Iceland, an old fellow who got mixed in the tale he told. Another had been with Vasco da Gama in India, to Calicut, a most friendly fellow who took Osberne down to where the five ships of Magellan's fleet lay, telling their names and tonnage in a proud kind of way.

"Such things," he said, "some one must bear in mind, lad, for soon men forget. Here is the *San Antonio* of a hundred and twenty tons. Next is the *Trinidad,* of ten tons less, which must be the flagship. Of ninety tons is the *Concepcion.* The *Victoria,* stoutest of all, runs to eighty-five tons. Then there is the *Santiago* of seventy-five tons. They say that a man from Italy, a noble named Pigafetta, will sail with the fleet, and he is one to write about all that he sees, day by day; but such men have no eye for matters that seamen look to. It may be that he will write and write, yet never tell the world if these ships are decked, how they are rigged; or if they are open and small, like the ships of Columbus. So mind well. You are a likely lad with a sharp eye."

Then he led Osberne to the town and the bazaar where they saw shops with rich things from India; pearls, spices, precious stones, silks, and perfumes. They saw men who went about carrying brass basins and mirrors hung to their chests, who cried out, "Who will be shaved? Who will be shaved?" and, having found a man, sat him down in the street and there shaved him. There were cooks going up and down, bearing braziers and fire, with food which they cooked. Others called out the names of fruits they offered for sale. Some with asses took about water-skins, selling water to those without wells. Some again drove milk goats which they milked in front of houses while people waited. In one place an old man, bald and full of wrinkles, held up a glass ball and told Osberne that for a coin he would tell him all that would befall him if he would gaze in the crystal, but Osberne laughed and went on, for that sort he had seen before, among the gipsies who went to Portsdown.

In one place they came upon a little knot of sailor-looking fellows. They were gathered about a loud-talking man, some of them sitting, some standing. At the edge of the crowd were grooms, pages, men-at-arms and an archer or two, so Osberne said to his companion that something of interest might be going forward, and cocked his ear to hear as they passed. Then he caught the name of Magellan, as said by the speaker who was a rough-looking fellow with yellow hair, one who frowned and whose thin lips were tightly drawn.

"Go on," called out an archer. "Tell us about this Magellan, Espinosa."

At that Osberne stood to listen, his companion with him.

"Magellan!" said the man called Espinosa, with a snarl. "I spit upon the fellow. A rascal Portuguese who would take the bread out of the mouths of honest Spaniards. Go not with his ships, I say. Do not demean yourselves to sail under the banner of a runaway from Portugal. A fellow of that sort deserves a taste of Spanish steel. One way and another, almost three months we have made him tarry here with his ships and soon the king will see that in wisdom he must withdraw the Portuguese and give the ships to be captained by Spaniards. Then shall all go well."

" I like not that kind of talk," whispered Osberne.

" It has been going on a long time. This is Espinosa, a well-known stirrer-up of trouble," said his companion.

" I greatly fear what may come of it," Espinosa went on, " for to give a fellow of no account and no breeding, such as is this Magellan, to give him, I say, mastery over Spanish men of birth, is a piece of work with evil in its train. An enemy of Spain, he is. And, I ask, who is there better to rule the fleet than the noble Juan de Cartagena? He is the man for me. He is the man for Spain. Magellan is a boaster and a man of little worth. Again I say it is certain that he is a traitor, and no true Spaniard would sail under his banner."

" So that is the way matters go," said Osberne, as they walked away.

" That is the way," answered his companion. " As for Espinosa, he is, as we say, one who would show a stranger the gallows before he shows him the town. But let us see the river."

Down by the river, a world of men seemed busy working about the fleet. But there were many who did not work, who stood about looking on and foretelling evil, mostly about mutiny that must come before the fleet had sailed many days.

As for the men of the *Seagull,* after the first day they had too much to do to listen to tales, because Sir Robert would stay no longer than it took to unload and to load again with merchandise for England. Then, all being ready, nothing would do but that he must give a feast because Hans and Osberne and Andrew were to leave him and take the world voyage. He was a man with a heart for his men, and he forgot rank in companionship. And when the sailors, his shipmates, were gathered together, Osberne looked at them and thought that it would be hard to pick out a finer crew, all of them so big-chested and ruddy, so rough-voiced and jolly. At the end of the feast Sir Robert gave a toast, standing up with his cup held high, and calling out, "To friendship and true manhood! To all courageous companions!" So they all stood up, then shook hands and wished each the other good luck, so that there was a great amount of laughing and talking and slapping of shoulders. Then Sir Robert took Osberne aside and told him how he would not forget his faithful service, and that while he would go as far as man might go in the world there would always be a place for him at Portsdown, not only a place but a friend too. On the next morning the *Seagull* sailed out of Seville and down the river, her flags flying, and two seamen beating a drum and playing a fife, others calling a farewell, and Sir Robert himself, big and strong, standing by the steersman; all of which Osberne and Andrew and Hans saw and heard from the river bank.

When it came to joining the fleet of Magellan nothing could have been easier. They had but to tell what they were and could do, Osberne a seaman, Hans and Andrew gunners, and no more was said, for there had been and still was no end of trouble in getting men together, as they soon learned. Indeed the man named Mendoza, who took down their names, told them so, and ordered them to go about doing what they could to pick up men. And as the three sat on the river bank a little later, wondering why men were so slow, Juan Zubista told them things that opened their eyes.

"I know nothing about ships, being a page," he said, "but I have heard that Alvarez, a spy for Portugal, tells everywhere that the ships are old and patched, their ribs soft as butter, and he would not go as far as the Canaries in them."

At the time they were sitting on the river bank eating oranges and throwing the skins into the water.

"True. The ships are old enough," agreed Andrew, " but that is not the worst of it. Saw a man ever worse fittings? Think of it. Here we go to sail round the wide world, but there are no more than five hammers for the crews of five ships."

" And only two grindstones," growled Hans. " He is a sorry barber that has only one comb."

" But they can spend good money for drums and tambourines," said Andrew. " A pretty pass when they think more of music than of work. Nor are there more than four ladles for the boiling of pitch. Sorrier outfitting I never saw."

" It is muddle and muddle," said Hans. " A trading man should know the truth of no gains without pains."

"And to think, when I asked for a hone to sharpen my knife, asking it of the carpenter, he said to his boy, ' Where is the hone?' Said I, ' The hone! Is there but one?' And he answered that there was one only. A smith in England would have more in his shop."

" You spoke of trading," said Osberne. "There in the trading end things are well enough. I have seen thousands of little bells, of little knives, of little scissors, of fishhooks, of combs, of little red caps, of brass basins, of looking-glasses. They are for the savages, to exchange for gold and rubies. If the ships had been fitted as the stores are, then there would be no reason to growl."

For a time no man spoke. It was Hans who broke the silence.

"That is because merchants look after the trading part, and

they have their heads screwed on the right way, as the saying goes. Merchants have given most of the money so have a keen eye on gains. But the king's men look after the ships and what care they how men fare?"

"Where I look for trouble most is in the men," said Andrew. "There is a Captain Serrao, and when I went on the ship to look about and see how things were, he was talking with a yellow-haired man whose name was Espinosa."

"A fellow with a loud voice and a rough manner of speaking?" asked Osberne.

"The very same," said Andrew. "Do you know him?"

"I have heard him talk," answered Osberne.

"Heard him!" said Andrew. "He has a voice like the white bull of Bashan. His whisper would shake a house. But somehow I like not his looks. There is that way of talking out of the side of his mouth and of looking aslant that I do not like. I heard him, I say. The whole ship could have heard. There he was, talking in a way to stir up trouble. This Captain Serrao was grumbling that the king's men had said that no more than one Portuguese should be on every ship, for they who are in charge are minded to keep the fleet Spanish. Then up spoke this Espinosa, telling Serrao to get Portuguese, to make them under-officers too. Then they began to name names, saying that Martin Magellan, cousin of the commander had been shipped. They named many others, all Portuguese; Barbosa, the brother-in-law of Magellan; a pilot, called Carvalho who had lived in the Brazils. And so they went."

"Yet that very man I heard in the town, telling sailors and men-at-arms and pages, that as long as Portuguese were on the ships, no proper Spaniard should join the fleet," said Osberne.

"A stirrer-up of trouble, this Espinosa," said Hans. "A maker of jealousy, and jealousy is worse than witchcraft."

"I heard him say these words: 'Who is there better to rule the fleet than the noble Juan de Cartagena?' The very words stick in my mind," said Osberne.

"Then look out for squalls, if this Espinosa sails with the fleet," put in Andrew.

"And sail he does," said Hans. "We talked together to-day and when it came out that I was a gunner you would have said that he was a long lost brother, by the way he loved me. And what things he told me with nods and winks! The time would come when he would be a captain of one of the ships, he said. He would rule the fleet, and what else I know not. So I see it all as a sorry business. The fleet at the beginning is a divided thing and many want to be head. And how hate is stirred up. There is Luis Mendoza, a king's man hated by Magellan and his friends."

"And this proud don, Juan de Cartagena, now put in as overseer-general," added Osberne. "No love is lost between him and Magellan."

"Also Antonio de Coca. Do not forget him," said Hans.

"What mean thing is it that the Spaniards called Magellan?" asked Andrew.

"A low person of no breeding," answered Osberne.

"That may well be," said Hans. "But there is a fire and a good fight about the man. So we shall see what we shall see. There must be trouble but we shall take no part. Let a man do the duty that lies nearest and all may go well with him."

"Yet it is a pretty kettle of fish, with the fleet already three months and a half past its sailing time," said Andrew. Then he rose and yawned. "Well," he went on, "we may as well do what we are to do and get what men we may, since a ship cannot sail without men." So the four arose and went to the town.

For two days thereafter Andrew and Hans were busy among the townsmen, and Osberne and Juan as busy among the boys, for at least one half of the two hundred and sixty-eight men were less than man's age at the sailing of the fleet. Andrew and Hans went about telling tales of voyages, how a man might buy gold for a fishhook, how a glass bead would be changed for more fish and fruit than a man could eat in a week, how the wind in the middle of the sea ran so smooth that sailors might sleep half the day and all the night, how jewels and pearls were to be picked up on the seashore as readily as stones. Osberne and Juan went to work another way, telling of adventure, and strange places, and giant fish, and lands where men might become princes. And the Spanish dons did a part among young men of good family so that forty of them joined the fleet without promise of pay, *sobresalienties* they were called. For the rest the crews were made up of negroes, Malays, Sicilians, Greeks, Genoese, Frenchmen, with a few who said nothing about their nation and less about themselves.

" A poor lot, but they may yet be beaten into shape," said Andrew. " But what would I not give to see Sir Robert making this voyage with his fellows."

So came the day, the twentieth of September, of the year 1519, when the five ships sailed out of the river. Osberne, with Andrew and Hans were on the *Trinidad,* the flagship, and their shipmates numbered fifty-nine besides themselves. Magellan himself was captain, a man who walked with a limp because of an old wound, one square built but not tall, quick of eye and swift of speech. On the moment of lifting the anchor Osberne was standing by the side of Hans, much wishing that his work might be with the guns or something of the kind, and trying to find a place to that end. And as he stood, Magellan passed, then stopped and thrust a finger at him.

"Have you no work to do that you stand gaping?" he asked, and before Osberne could answer a word he added, "Go. There are two cows in the ship. See to them. One work is good as another. Feed them. Clean them."

Then he passed on and stood by the steersman. So Osberne swallowed his anger, for he had no mind to go to sea to look after cows, but he remembered what Andrew had said about the duty of a man lying nearest him. But there was this. The cows were in a place on deck, and while Osberne made a bed of straw for them, and put food in the rack, there was time to see things. No sight, he thought, could have been more gay than the river with its many boats dressed in blue and scarlet, with awnings of shining white, and its richly dressed men and women, and the boats dancing on the little waves made by the ships. On shore the people were lined like an army, and the air was athrob with ringing of bells, and the sound of trumpets, and the noise of guns. Banners fluttered from every house and people had lit great bonfires which blazed high. Close behind the *Trinidad,* so close that Osberne could see its captain, Mendoza plainly for he stood in the forefront of the ship, came the *Victoria,* very brave-looking with flags, and with boats rowing alongside in which were the captain's friends, some of them being towed for a little way by ropes held by seamen. From the river banks men-at-arms made salute, and the farewell was more hearty than that given to Magellan and his *Trinidad* because of the jealousy between Portuguese and Spaniard. But the greatest roar went up for the *San Antonio* that sailed out

third, with Captain Cartagena in purple cloak and wide-
brimmed hat looking more like a king than the captain of a
ship. A great banner of silk flew from his masthead. Next
came the *Concepcion,* its forty-four men standing in the rigging and Captain Quesado on the deck with a page on his right
hand and another on his left, each carrying a banner. The
ship's two bombards roared out a farewell to the people on
shore. But small notice was taken of the little *Santiago,* for its
Captain Serrao was a Portuguese. And as the ships moved
stately down the river, swift sail-boats played about the five
ships, darting this way and that, going far ahead then turning to
come back, then shooting between ship and ship. So the fleet
dropped out of the river and into the open sea to find a light
breeze that made a smooth swell; and the flags fluttered most
bravely; and the blocks began to creek and groan; and the
splash of blue water against the ship's sides made merry music.

So at last the voyage was well begun and merrily everything
went until they came to the Island of Tenerife, of the Canaries,
where they dropped anchor and all hands went ashore to get
wood and water for the ships. The work being done, and the
wind light, the crews of the five ships played awhile on shore,
some swimming, some wrestling, a few fencing with light
sticks to serve as swords, while the officers and captains looked
on. But, as many noticed, while a little group of them stood
around Juan de Cartagena, Magellan and Serrao walked together, not looking at the sports.

"I have no liking for that kind of business," said Andrew
to Osberne. "It has a flavor of trouble. This business of
Spanish against Portuguese will never do."

"That is not the worst of it," said Osberne. "Last night
there sailed into this place a caravel from Spain and this morn-

ing it is not here. Juan told me that a man went aboard while we were all on shore, asleep, and knocked at the cabin door. The slave Enrique woke his master and the stranger went into the cabin. What took place there no one knows, but there were high words with the admiral storming and saying things about traitors."

" That looks bad," said Andrew. " These men act like dogs about to fight, eyeing one another, going near and yet not too near, scorning and loathing. See them now. There you have the Admiral and Captain Serrao walking near by Juan de Cartagena, but that grand captain turning his back. It is a storm brewing. And, mark my words, the storm will break soon."

The two were sitting in the admiral's boat as they talked, and close to it, drawn up on the beach, lay the boat of Captain Juan de Cartagena, nor were they five yards apart. Along the beach were other boats belonging to the ships, and every boat had its rowers near by or in the boat. At a sign from the admiral, Miguel de Roasa of the *Victoria* blew a long and shrill whistle, then three blasts, as a sign that all should go aboard, so men started running down the beach. Magellan and Serrao, being quick walkers, were at their boats and seated before some of the men had got ready their oars. But Captain Juan de Cartagena, with his friends Mendoza and Quesada, and a couple of others, walked more leisurely, talking and laughing the while. So it came about that they were the last to reach their boats. Noting their leisureliness the admiral frowned, then, when Captain Cartagena stood at his boat's side, arranging first his cloak, then his sword, next looking to his dagger, Magellan called across, somewhat roughly, " As I am a living man, as captain I sought to be quicker than my men. Now, as admiral, it seems that it is easier for me to be quicker than my captains."

Captain Cartagena laughed lightly, then said, " High noon and a hot sun make not for speed, Admiral. *An ounce of patience is worth a pound of brains* and if a man lacks the last he may at least cultivate the first."

So saying, he stepped into the boat and took his seat. For a little while the admiral bit his lip, then he rose to his feet and flashed into hot temper. " Ha! " he cried. " Do you insult me? "

" Why all that heat, dear Admiral? " answered Cartagena. " It is but a proverb of Spain and nothing more. Spain is full of proverbs and sayings. There is another that runs, *He who loses his temper is in the wrong.* Another says, *Hasty climbers have sudden falls,* dear Admiral. Another says, *A man in a passion rides a horse that runs away with him.* There are hundreds of such sayings, my dear Admiral. One says, *Suspicion may be no fault, but showing it is a great one.* They are but words. But one of the best of the sayings runs, *A merry companion is music on a journey* and for my part I love music."

" Listen, Juan de Cartagena — " roared Magellan.

" Pardon me, Admiral," interrupted the don. " You forget. I am captain of the *San Antonio,* joint master of the fleet with Admiral Ferdinand Magellan, made by our gracious king bearer of the Royal Standard, and Knight of the Order of *Santiago.* So Captain Juan de Cartagena, if it please your honor."

" Last night a bearer brought me a letter from Spain," said the admiral, thoroughly angry. " There are traitors in the ships, it warns. ' Keep a good watch,' it says, ' because certain captains when in Spain told their friends that some are resolved not to obey.' So I put it to you, Captain Cartagena — "

" Thank you for the title, Admiral," said Cartagena mockingly.

" I put it to you to nip this business in the bud," the admiral went on. " You I hold responsible. I have written back that I am a servant of the king and have offered the emperor my life."

Having made an end he sat down and ordered the rowers to work.

" Thank you, Admiral," answered Cartagena. " There is another saying in Spain, and it runs thus, *Accusing is proving when malice and force sit as judges."*

Before night the report of that talk on the beach ran through the fleet, and Espinosa was the news-bearer. Before two days another outbreak came, and then men began to take sides. For Cartagena, going on deck one morning, saw that the course of the *Trinidad* lay along the coast of Africa instead of to the southwest, thereupon he turned his ship and ran alongside the admiral's vessel, and, seeing Magellan, called out, " What is the course? "

" Follow my flag and ask no questions," roared back the admiral. " Fall into place behind."

But Cartagena had no mind to do that.

" If the course be changed," he called, " the rules under which we sail call for a meeting of captains and pilots. Besides, I know these seas and there is no wisdom in a course along the African coast."

" Back to your place," called Magellan. " It is for you to follow my flag by day and my lantern by night."

" If you do not know, then I must tell you, Admiral," shouted Captain Cartagena. " Thus we delay. We miss the good winds to Brazil. We sail to the place of foul weather."

" Back to your place, sir," repeated Magellan. "It is for you to follow, not to question."

And into foul weather they slid. For twenty days the ships lay in sight of one another, not a breeze stirring the flags. So still was the sea that all about the ships lay the refuse they had thrown overboard. Not ten sea miles during the twenty days did they advance. Out of the sea the hot sun climbed, day after day, baking the ships until the pitch burned the feet of the men. Under a sky like brass the men lay about the decks and gasped for air. And the water became hot, then foul. And it was found that the wine casks had burst so that on some of the ships good food was spoiled and had to be thrown overboard; then sharks came and swam about and the men could no longer swim to cool themselves.

Then came a storm on a day that had been cloudless in the morning.

It came with a sudden gale after gray clouds had piled across the sky. The sea turned to flying spray, then came lower clouds that flew, and the light of day changed to sickly yellow. The *Trinidad,* struck by a great wave, leaned over until her yards touched the sea and she would not obey her helm. The ships flew across a half-dark world of waters while sea and sky roared, and great flashes of lightning leaped from west to east, one following another so close that a cascade of fire seemed to fall out of the heavens. Under bare poles they ran until they came near to the equator, and then the storms ended and the wind dropped. Then came rain, weeks of rain, rain which they could not catch for drink having no vessels for that end. Not ten miles a day did they sail. And both food and water had given out, so that Osberne, on the *Trinidad* was sick at heart as he took around to each man a pint of water each morning, and a pound and a half of bread, for other food there was none. What had not been spoiled by the heat, or lost during the storm, had been ruined by the rain. Osberne was sick at heart because strong men went down on their knees and begged for another mouthful of water, sometimes wept like children because of the pain of hunger.

But all that pain and suffering did nothing to stay the fever of hate that ran through the hearts of the men. Indeed, as Hans said, " The hate grows because men think the trouble might have been missed had the fleet sailed the course Cartagena wished."

That hate broke out one morning when the *San Antonio* hailed and saluted as the laws of the fleet held should be done. The quartermaster called out, as the two ships drew close, " God save you captain and master and good companion."

Magellan at the time took no notice, but stood staring out to the west. A daily affair, he took it as a matter of course just as any man hearing a thing said a thousand times hears it not at all the thousandth time and one. But Espinosa heard, and took note that the title of captain-general had not been used.

" Strange how men forget," he said. " The quartermaster must be told to call out in proper fashion. It is nothing between equals, but sailors are a rough lot and respect must be kept."

Instantly Magellan flew into a rage. Leaning far over the side and shaking his fist, he shouted across the lane of water, " Cartagena! Hear this! By my title I am to be called. Captain-general. I am captain-general, with power of rope or ax over those who disobey. Bear that in mind, or, by all the saints, we shall have things to settle that are greater than titles."

At a sign from Cartagena, the steersman of the *San Antonio* had kept the ships close together so that the answer could be heard by every man.

"Magellan," answered Cartagena, "you have been saluted by the best one of my men, and if you do not like it then next time you shall be saluted by one of my pages. And so enough."

"By my title I shall be called," roared Magellan.

"Good," answered Cartagena, mockingly, and made a mock salute. "We have one of those sayings you do not like which runs that it is not the surplice that makes the parson or clerk. Neither is it the title that makes the master."

"That is your Spanish tongue, dagger pricking," said Espinosa to Magellan. "Let it pass, Admiral. He will be sorry."

"It is a tongue that I shall silence and a dagger that I shall make blunt," answered Magellan, full of black anger.

But by that time the *San Antonio* had dropped astern and into line. Nor for three days did the ship make any morning salute.

On the third day something happened. As Osberne went about with the water, giving out the portions, a starving sailor snatched the measure from his hand and swallowed down the contents, thus taking more than his share. It was no new thing to Osberne, nor had he said anything about such deeds knowing that there is no law for starving men. But Espinosa saw and ordered the man tied up to the mast for whipping. So there he hung in the hot sun, half-dead, until Osberne and Andrew begged that he be released.

"It must be a whipping or a court-martial," answered Espinosa, then stopped suddenly as a thought came. "I shall see the admiral," he said, and went away.

"Now what notion is in his black heart?" said Andrew.

Others wondered too, seeing the two officers who stood on the upper deck, talking closely. Nor did they talk for long before a sailor ran up a flag for the fleet to see, and so all men knew it for a sign that a court-martial was to he held.

CHAPTER III

The Court-Martial and the Mutiny

SEEING the signal, the five ships drew together, and every sailor knew a time of pleasure seeing the boats, with the officers, row to the *Trinidad,* for the day was a quiet one and the ships sailed slow.

But, as men saw, between some of the captains there was a coldness when greetings were said and while they took their places in the court that was to be held on the after-deck. When they were seated, men-at-arms came with their pikes and swords and stood in a half-circle. Captain Cartagena sat between Antonio de Coca and Mendoza, all three in their finery, each with a page behind him. A priest stood near. Magellan and Serrao sat at the head of a table, both glum-looking, and behind the admiral stood Juan de Zubista holding a banner as sign of the king's power given to Magellan. That was the judges' end of the court.

The other side of the court was sorrier to see. There was the sailor who was on trial, a lad of no more than eighteen years, thin and weak and haggard. Andrew guarded him, and on Andrew's left stood Osberne. Six men-at-arms were ranged behind, and at one end of the line of armed men was Espinosa.

When a page blew a trumpet the trial began, with Espinosa telling the judges what it was all about and how the sailor stood accused of taking stores that should be guarded. He set great value, he said, on the loyalty of the crew. He told how the king looked to every man to help his fellow. He testified how the sailor had stolen water. Then he said a great deal about Magellan's heart and life having been given to the king and this voyage. It was all very dull, and very slow, and very long, so that many who heard had to stifle a yawn. Then questions were put to the sailor; why he did this and that, was he loyal to the king, had he stolen before, and much more, some of the questions having very little and some of them nothing at all to do with the matter. The lad, though most wretchedly clad and shod, a mere thing of skin and bone, bore himself with pride. Once, while the judges talked among themselves with Espinosa busy with them, Andrew whispered to Osberne, "Even the judges are weary of the matter."

When the judges sat back in their seats again, Magellan said to the sailor, questioning, "You heard the orders, and how men would have so much bread and a pint of water each day?"

"I heard, Admiral," came the answer. "But a hungry stomach has no ears."

At that Magellan frowned, but Cartagena laughed a little, not loud or roughly, but half to himself. Yet Magellan heard and saw.

"Captain Cartagena, I see nothing for merriment in this," said Magellan, very rapid in his speech.

"Nor I, Admiral," came the answer. "There are times when, even in laughter, the heart is sorrowful."

"This is no case for laughter or for grief," said Magellan. "It is the law that speaks."

"But when drums speak, laws hold their tongues," answered Cartagena, lifting his head. "This has been like unto war, our troublesome venture, and not alone this lad, but many of us have been punished."

"What have the other judges to say?" asked Magellan, looking away from Cartagena.

"It may be well to let the lad go," said Antonio de Coca. "He has had punishment enough and it is a poor business to hang a man for a pint of water. Besides, a dead man can do nothing for us. A living man may yet do much. In the case I do not care to judge a punishment."

"Well enough said," put in Cartagena. "Who are we to sit in judgment in such a case? Indeed, in one way of looking at the matter some of us who are judges might as well be on trial."

"What do you mean?" asked Magellan, his face darkly red.

"It is but a thought said aloud," put in Antonio de Coca, wishing to steer past trouble between Magellan and Cartagena.

At the other end of the court Andrew whispered to Osberne, "It looks to me that we are to have another storm. You may see for yourself the pride of Cartagena and the growing anger of the admiral. The two play trick against trick."

"Admiral," said Cartagena. "Where there is small fault, there pardons count for little. We do no great thing in pardoning. Let us be men and put the matter out of the way. The man's fault is feather-light. Indeed, had he been a sailor on my *San Antonio* I would have let the matter pass with a word."

"So also I," said Mendoza.

"And I," added Antonio de Coca.

"My mind, too, runs to forgiveness in this case," said Serrao.

"It is not the crime but the example," said Espinosa.

Of that remark Magellan took no notice. He sat for a little while drumming his fingers on the table, then said to the prisoner, "Go. You are free this time. But do better. And tell your fellows that it is well to remember that in me rests the power of rope and ax, whoever the wrong-doer, be he man or master, page or captain. So go."

Glad enough to do so, Andrew led the man away, at a sign from the admiral.

For a little while the officers talked in a general way but Magellan seemed downcast and silent.

"What did you mean?" he asked Cartagena. "What did you mean when you said that? What was it?"

"I said this," answered Cartagena, "Who are we to sit in judgment when, in a way of looking at it, some of the judges may as well themselves be on trial, if fair is fair."

"In my country we use plain words and do not talk in riddles," said Magellan frowning and drumming on the table harder than before.

"Plain then let it be," said Cartagena. "You, Admiral, have been at fault. Had the agreed course been followed we would not have met the calms. Had we not been becalmed our water would not have given out. We would have been now on the coasts of America. Our men would not have been starved. To be plain, Admiral, the fault is yours. And were justice done, you would be on trial. Indeed you have been on trial because I, your appointed adviser, privately have condemned you as one not worthy to hold the office you hold. So, I have been plain."

The speech had not been half said when Magellan rose to his feet and stood, one hand on the table, the other at the hilt of his sword. His eyes were flashing angrily and his teeth gritted. Cartagena had not moved in his seat but sat looking at his admiral with open clear eyes and with a smile on his lips. Then, suddenly, all about was a hubbub. Magellan took a step forward, throwing over the table as he did so. His two hands went out and caught Cartagena by the throat. Espinosa and some of the men at arms gathered around the two and when Magellan shouted, " You are my prisoner! Arrest him!" they drew swords or leveled their pikes.

" You, Captain Mendoza, will keep watch over him day and night," ordered Magellan, and his rage was terrible to see. " Cartagena is your prisoner to be in chains on the *Victoria*. You, Antonio de Coca, shall be Captain of the *San Antonio* until I make other change." Then his eyes chanced to fall on Osberne. " You, a fellow who cannot keep men from stealing water, shall go with the prisoner as his guard. Should he escape, should he as much as hold word with another man, then look to your head. Guard him day and night. Stay down in the hold with him. So away."

Thus ended the court-martial, and thus it came about that Osberne, day-long and night-long lived in the black hold, seeing neither sun nor sea, breathing foul air with his prisoner, crawled over at night by rats and vermin, not daring for his life's sake to talk to the man he guarded. Only for an hour at sunset could he go on deck and fill his lungs with clean air while a man-at-arms took his place. In that miserable hole he could see his prisoner by a chink of light that came through a crack in the hold and the man looked deadly and terrible. Yet never a word of complaint fell from him. So the ships went into the great bay of Brazil, loading there with fresh provisions and sweet water, then started again to sail south along the coast of America, but Osberne saw nothing of the land. The fleet lay in Rio de la Plata while some sought for a passage to the west, but Osberne did not see that river. They lay for two days in a bay because the *San Antonio* had sprung a leak, but all the time Osberne was in the dark with his prisoner. Nor did the lad see the sea and sky and land until the last day of March, of the year 1520, when Cartagena was taken on deck and chained to the mast, and Osberne, white and thin because of his long confinement, found himself freed from his charge.

He saw a gray land, a gray sky, and a gray water in a lonely bay, and thought it the saddest country he had ever set eyes upon. Men told him the land was Patagonia and that the place had been named San Julian Bay. When they told him, not in any straight way, but by scraps now and other scraps of talk then, they grumbled. He found that not his food alone had been stinted of late, but the food of all the fleet. He learned that the fleet would stay there all the winter and that the ships would be cleaned and repaired, and that fish would be caught and dried and packed away in order that all might be well for the great voyage, for they would start south again in the spring. Then he heard strange tales, how the Indians were twelve feet high and more, how they swallowed and drew forth again their arrows, how they leaped twenty feet at a step and much more. But when he asked, he could find none who had seen the Indians close.

One thing made him glad, and it was that his quartermaster told him to go on board the *San Antonio,* that ship being most out of repair. So he went, with others, and to make his day most joyful, he saw Andrew, and heard him say, in a rough tone of voice for the others to hear, and pretending to be hard, "Fellow, why stand there like a stuck pig? We have guns to get out and to clean and to set ashore. Move yourself."

Gladly then Osberne went to work, and presently, when no others were near, Andrew came and grasped his hand.

"What a sorry business all this is," he said. "Here we have a new thing, with more of the Portuguese in charge, and more of the king's men put down."

"What now?" asked Osberne. "I know nothing, having been so long in the hold with no man saying a word to me."

"Then you cannot know that Magellan's cousin, Alvaro de Mesquita has been made Captain of the *San Antonio,* and that Antonio de Coca has been stripped of his power. It is so," said Andrew, very serious.

"I know nothing of that and am sorry to learn it, Andrew."

"Well, lad, there will be worse to come and soon. Tell me in what cabin you have been put."

"In that of Juan de Lorriago the Basque," answered Osberne. "There are others in it."

"The Basque is a sound fellow with a heart of gold," went on Andrew. "Maybe you can give him a hint to have his dagger ready. Maybe you will have no such chance. But watch. As for yourself, hide somewhere and take care of your own skin. When the time comes do the duty that lies nearest at hand. Watch your own liberty. Let the masters fight their own fights and let us keep cool heads."

"What is at the bottom of all this, Andrew?" asked Osberne, half-dazed.

"I wish I knew. But I hear hints, one here and another there. I have heard men whispering, telling one another that the stroke will fall to-night, but what that stroke is I do not know. But the Spaniards have no love for the captain of this ship and I put two and two together thinking there will be mutiny. I know nothing because I stand on neither side. Mark you, both sides have their merits, both their evils. Truth is not with one. But no more. Here comes Mesquita." Then Andrew spoke roughly again, knowing that at the least sign of friendship he and Osberne would be separated. "Be not so slow, fellow," he said. "We have hot work to do. If you work no better I shall get another one to help."

For the rest of that day Andrew and Osberne had no chance for private talk because men were sent from other ships, and much work had to be done; then, at sundown they were called elsewhere and taken away in the boats, most of them to the *Trinidad,* Andrew among them. But because of the warning Osberne took his blanket and slept in the shadow of the bulwark with one eye open as the saying is.

In the middle watch, when the world was still, he heard the faint sound of muffled oars, so lifted his head and saw three boats coming, loaded with men. Now and then he caught the glint of steel as the moonlight fell on sword or armor, but who the men were he could not tell until two of the crew, Spaniards both, crept up and looked over the side, then whispered together. One of them carried a stout rope, and both wore swords.

" The plan works well," said one, so low that Osberne could barely catch the words. " In the first boat is Captain Quesada, Juan de Cartagena whom they have released, and Juan Sebastian del Cano. The plan is that they will swing round to the larboard side. Antonio de Coca and Luis del Molino and Mendoza will attack from the starboard. The others will board where they can."

" It goes well thus far," whispered the other. " Most of the crew who know nothing sleep like the dead. The others are ready and armed. Those we cannot trust are locked up safe. Captain Quesada has said that a dagger must put Lorriaga out of the way. Maybe also his friends Fernandez and Rodriguez and the boy called Osberne will be slit open. They are all Magellan men."

" This Diego Hernandez too is to be watched. But he is not locked in the cabin with Lorriaga and the others."

For a while the two watched the boats and Osberne could hardly stop himself from looking up to see how near they were. And he wondered how he could manage to get to the cabin and free Lorriaga. But the noise made by the boats took the two men to another part of the ship, and he saw them looking over the side. Then, going on finger tips and toes, crouched like an animal and keeping well in the deep shadow, the lad crept to the opposite companionway and when the time seemed ripe he made a quick dash across the open deck and so was down the few steps in a flash of time. It brought his heart to his mouth when he knew that he had run into danger, for a man with a sword stepped out of the blackness and whispered, " Who comes? Friend or enemy? "

" Stay me not," said Osberne. " The boats are come and you are wanted on deck."

But the man held Osberne and would have dragged him to a corner to see him by the light of a ship's lantern that stood behind a cask.

"Play not the fool," said Osberne. "There is Quesada come, with the others. I must see to the Lorriaga matter."

He said that by chance but it was enough. The man on watch ran into another part of the ship, but to where Osberne could not see. But listening, he heard whispers, then the noise of feet, also the soft sound of steel touching steel lightly, so he guessed that armed men who had been hidden were going on deck. Indeed, as he made his way to the part of the ship where Lorriaga and the others were locked in he brushed against a man or two. But being at the cabin door there was a new danger, a sailor on guard with a naked sword, and before Osberne could gather his wits, the sword's point pricked his throat.

"What do you here?" asked the guard.

"A message," said Osberne, on the spur of the moment. "Play not the fool with swords at this time."

"But my orders," said the sailor.

"Things go not by rule and order now," answered Osberne, whispering. "Here is Quesada, and the others with him. I am sent to look after this matter and you are to go on deck."

At that moment they heard the noise of trampling feet above.

"Haste," said Osberne. "Or do you not like the new job?"

"Like it?" answered the guard. "I like not this standing in the dark to go in and murder comrades in cold blood."

"Then on deck and haste," said Osberne, and the sailor went running.

As soon as there was quiet Osberne found the lock by feeling, and the key was in it. He threw back the bolt and opened the door, so found himself in pitchy darkness, but he knew the place and where the men slept; so touched one and another and whispered. "Treason, Juan Lorriaga! Mutineers are taking the ship and you are doomed to die. Wake, Antonio Fernandez! It is I, Osberne. Goncalo Rodriguez, wake and up. And you, Diego Diaz. They have taken the ship and our lives are in danger."

In an instant the men were up, feeling about for their clothes and for such things as would do for weapons, asking questions the while. But all that they could find were sticks, and a short bar of iron, for neither sword nor dagger nor knife could be had.

"What plans do you know?" asked Lorriaga.

"None but the plan to do away with you fellows," answered Osberne.

"Then to the captain's cabin!" ordered Lorriaga.

So they went running, the five of them, sometimes stumbling and sometimes knocking against head beams until they came nigh to Captain Alvaro de Mesquita's cabin, then saw that they were too late to help. For with chains on his hands and feet, and under a strong guard, the captain was being led away. They heard Gaspar Quesada say, "Chain him in Geronimo Guerra's cabin with a guard of four men. Kill any who come near. The rest of you on deck."

"By all that is holy!" said Lorriaga. "We must do what we can. Come, fellows!"

Quick as a lizard Lorriaga turned, then snatched a lantern from a careless man-at-arms and led the way to the forward end of the ship, his companions hard on his heels, while the mutineers, talking among themselves and laughing because of

the surprise, climbed by the ladder amidships to the deck.
Thus it came about that Osberne and Lorriaga and the three
were on deck before any great number of the mutineers had
got out of the hold. But in the dim moonlight they saw many
sailors and men-at-arms here and there. Also they were met
by the faithful Diego Hernandez who ran to Lorriaga crying,
" We are betrayed! We are betrayed! To arms! to arms! "

Lorriaga, naked to the waist and unarmed, was like a tiger.
Down the deck he went, the others with him, six men against
a hundred and more. A little group of men-at-arms seeing
him coming brought down their pikes to the level, but Lorriaga leaped, flinging himself on to the shafts of the pikes so
that the points of them fell, and into the breach thus made
Osberne and the others ran. There were blows given and
taken, with the pikemen too near to do harm, and Lorriaga
striking right and left. Nor were the others less full of fire.
Down went many a man, and some stood doing nothing, not
knowing but that the whole crew of the *San Antonio* had
broken loose to repel boarders.

" Call the crew, Hernandez! " roared Lorriaga, and the
quartermaster sounded his whistle, but at that moment a dozen
of the mutineers sprang at him and down he went. But Lorriaga had fought a way to Quesada by that time. " Traitor!
Leave the ship! " he cried, then attacked the Spaniard with bare
fists though the Basque was half naked and the captain armed
with sword and dagger and breastplate. Also others of the
six fought furiously. Osberne found himself engaged with two
men, wrestling and striking, and while he fought he saw, in
flashes, other things. He saw four men bear Lorriaga down,
and saw Quesada with uplifted dagger strike at the Basque,
saw the blood spurt too. Then he saw no more for he knew

himself to be falling overboard, his attackers with him, the three locked together. Down in the sea he went and in the water there was too much to do for all of them. So they struck out, each for himself. But Osberne, having no mind to return to the ship, made for the shore. As he swam his mind grew clear so that he could weigh matters somewhat, and it seemed to him that there could not be more danger on land than on the ships, in spite of hunger and savages and strange animals. At last he touched the sand, though the swim must have taken him an hour at least. Seaward he could see nothing except two of the ships like shadows. But the air felt warm enough, and under a bank there was shelter from the light wind. So he scraped together some sand and made a sort of bed for himself and it amazed him much, when the light came, to find that he had slept comfortably.

Now that morning Osberne had the strangest of adventures. Being hungry, the first thing was to get food, but it had been a hungry voyage and he and pain of the stomach were no strangers. But above all he wished to keep out of sight of the ships until such time as he knew how things were. So he went around a point of land which hid him from prying eyes and where a narrow arm of the sea ran up into the land, thinking that a little river might fall into the sea at that place. As the tide was low many rocks stuck out from the sand and he saw on them black mussels not different from those he had gathered many a hundred time on the shore at Portsdown. So there was a something to stay the stomach. But he found more. There were mushrooms on the shore. Also a bush bore fruit of a kind he had not seen before, black and sweet and of the size of a small cherry, with three or four seeds. As the tide came up he saw that the bay was full of fish and thought how good a meal might be made if he had fire. So being a little refreshed and feeling stronger, and the sun having dried his breeches, for he had no other clothes, he thought to climb the hill, going up on the side furthest from the sea, because he knew himself for a deserter which meant the rope or the ax, were he seen and caught.

When he had climbed out of the lowlands he found himself on the edge of a great plain, a very sea of grass, and, to the west was a far-reaching hill that looked like a stair or step. As he looked, he saw the greatest bird in the world, as he thought, which came running with outstretched wings, and, seeing him, turned another way. So large it seemed that the sight of it took his breath. The creature ran to the west then stopped, standing with head raised high, but whether it stopped because of the sight of him, or because of something else, he did not know, nor could guess. Shy and wary it seemed, also a little confused. Osberne saw the creature leap high, run in a little circle, then in a zigzag course; next stand, stagger, fall. He also saw the arrow that had transfixed it, but only for a moment when the bird stood outlined against the sky. But no man was in sight, nor as much as a bush in which a man might hide, so he knew, as a man used to the way of the countryside knows, that whoever had shot lay hid in a hollow place not far from the great bird. He also knew that whosoever shot the arrow must have seen him, must indeed be even then watching him, so to run would be useless. So he lifted high his hands and stood awhile, then slowly turned himself about with his back to the unseen eyes, and so around until he faced the first way. Next he took four paces forward, his hands still held in the air, and again slowly turned about to show his helplessness and trust. After that he stood. Another four

· ATO · GREETS · OSBERNE ·

strides he made, and again turned himself round, and stood again. Then, as it seemed, out of the ground a figure rose, though Osberne knew it had been hid in the hollow; and it was a slim and well-built figure of a young man who carried a bow, with an arrow already to the string. So straighter than before Osberne stretched his arms up, and slower he turned, though not without worry of mind and some fear, but he took no more steps. And as a dog that would be friendly with another narrows the distance between, so did the Indian lad. At last he stood face to face with Osberne, looking him in the eyes. Then, laying down his bow, he placed his right hand on Osberne's shoulder, then with his left took Osberne's right wrist, but gently; next he set Osberne's right hand on his own shoulder and so stood. "Ato. Ato," he said, over and over again, so Osberne came to think Ato to be the Indian's name and named his own, tapping his breast with his left hand and saying, "Osberne, Osberne." Next came an act that bound Osberne fast to his new-found companion, for the Indian handed to him his bow and arrow, and having done that walked away some ten paces, threw up his hands as Osberne had done and so left himself at the mercy of the white lad. After a little thought Osberne took the arrow and stuck it barb first into the ground. So there they were, bound in friendship without a word.

Long afterwards, when Osberne thought of that day, he could hardly bring himself to believe that they spoke no word that the other could understand, except to name one another when needful to bespeak attention. He could not believe that they did not talk, because of the perfect understanding between them. Ato led him to a stream that ran through a narrow gorge, and pulled aside some bushes that hid a cavelike hole that ran about four feet into the cliff. There burned a fire, not larger than a man's hand, and Ato fed it until it glowed. Then he brought from some hiding place a piece of meat that tasted like venison and which Osberne came to know as the flesh of an animal called the guanaco. They cooked it and made a good meal. Then they went to work cutting up and preparing for food the ostrich that Ato had shot. Once Ato made Osberne understand that they should try a foot race, which they did, and the white lad gasped with wonder seeing how fast flew the Indian. But with bow and arrow they were more equal. So, near the end of the day Osberne wondered how there could be all that peace, while in the bay and on the ships there was nothing but pain and cruelty. A little later he felt much as a strange dog might feel if found by a boy eager to win his family to a liking for the animal. For Ato took him many miles, over a low hill, and there they came upon the camp of the tribe. For a long time Osberne stood on the side of the hill while Ato talked, but no man there took a weapon, so Osberne judged that all was well. Then Ato came and led him, and some brought soft furs, others rugs made of a yellow and white kind of wool of a sort new to him, and one showed him a tent made of skins, so he went in, gladly fell on the skin bed and slept.

But in the quiet of the night he awoke to hear the noise of bombards and his mind flew to Andrew and to Hans and Juan, his friends. Was it right, he asked himself, that he should be there when they faced danger? Had he played the part of a coward and a traitor? Was he a true friend who would run away instead of standing ready to lay down his life for his friend? If there was hard fighting between the ships, as there promised to be, should he not share it? He could not thrust such thoughts out of his mind, so he sat up, quietly he thought, but not so quiet but that he aroused Ato. Then came an effort to make Ato understand that he must leave.

"I thank you good and kindly folk," he said over and over again, knowing that Ato understood nothing, nor did he understand the things that Ato said in his turn.

But perhaps the Indian understood more than Osberne thought. What he did was to lead the white lad out of the camp, but not until he had said something to two men in another tent. Then, being a little apart from the camp, and the moonlight shining fair enough, Ato ran down into a hollow which Osberne had not seen before, and there gave a low whistle. Looking, Osberne saw three or four animals new to him, slim and graceful and of the size of an ass, but with long necks and small heads. Two of them Ato chose, then slipped into their jaws a hide slip like the reins of a horse, but with no bit. At first Osberne thought that the Indians used them as horses and wondered how such slim-legged creatures could bear the weight of a man, but he soon found his mistake. For Ato came running by the side of one of the animals, the other trotting behind. Then, placing Osberne's hand on the shoulder of the creature, the wool of which was soft to the touch, he signed to the lad to do as he did. So Osberne looked, heard Ato make a clicking noise, and saw the animal start off going lightly and swiftly. The help to the runner was like that which a man gains when running by the side of a horse holding fast to a stirrup leather. Thus they sped over the land, far swifter than a man not so helped could run, and in time came to the seaside where the ships lay. When they stood quiet and still Osberne could hear a great noise of singing and shouting on board the *San Antonio,* and now and then the noise of a bombard, so he burned the more to know what could be afoot and somewhat scolded himself for running away.

Next he knew that Ato was saying things, but the words held no meaning for him.

"You have been kind and I thank you," said Osberne.

Then the Indian said something, and Osberne, though he wondered much what it could be, thought it meant, "You must come back to us when you can."

"I have friends on the ships," said Osberne, knowing that the Indian could not understand.

When the Indian spoke again, which he did in few words, Osberne took it to mean, "If your friends are dead, then you have a place with us."

So Osberne put his right hand on the left shoulder of Ato, and Ato put his right hand on Osberne's left shoulder for a moment. Then Osberne said, "Farewell," and the Indian answered, "Adayar," which the white lad took to mean, "God be with you."

By that time the gray in the sky began to lighten in the east, so Osberne stepped into the water, waded knee-deep, turned again to wave to Ato who stood shading his eyes with his right hand, then he struck out breasting the light waves.

But he had not made many strokes towards the *San Antonio* when he changed his mind and turned towards the *Trinidad*. For there both Hans and Andrew might be, and those he wished to see. It lay furthest out to the mouth of the harbor, and, low as he was in the water, it seemed to be very far away, so far that at one time he feared that the cold of the water would cramp him before he reached the ship. But the food and the day's rest and the night's sleep stood him in good service so that he reached the ship, then hung awhile to the anchor chain until he had rested. And being somewhat stronger he went up the chain and over the side, but fell on to the deck because of the weakness of his knees. A bitter anger with himself filled him because he could not help sobbing, though it was not weeping but utter weariness. So worn and spent he was that he could not rise at first when the guard came running and cried, " What do you here? " Then he felt the point of a sword on his neck. " Up and give account of yourself," said the voice. Next he was pulled roughly to his feet and stood there shaking, not with fear, but because of his weariness.

" The fellow swam well," said a second guard. " But what chance for an arrow in his head? "

" I am Osberne of the *San Antonio*," he found breath to say. " No traitor neither. I fell over the ship's side in the fight and went to land."

" Yes," said another who had joined them. " I know the lad. Nor is there anything against him except that he did not testify against me when I stole the water. Nor would I trouble the admiral with such small matters on such a time as this. Let him rest awhile. Even if he would he could do no mischief here. And swimming to the *Trinidad* would be no traitor act. He would have gone to the *San Antonio*."

" Ay, let him go to his friends," said another.

" Only you must not hide," warned the first man. " Show yourself freely and speak out."

" Nor forget that there is peril in whispers," added the other.

" As Andrew's help he will be gladly welcomed," said the first, whose name was Martin Ros. " Come, lad. I will lead you to him."

So Osberne followed, and as soon as Andrew clapped eyes on him he called out, in his rough way, as if angry, " Boy! No slow work now or it's the rope's end for you. I care nothing about how you came. But go and eat. Tell the cook I sent you. Eat what your skin will hold for I have no place for weak men and there is trouble afoot." But the roughness the lad did not mind, knowing Andrew's way, and a fine meal he made when he found the food.

CHAPTER IV

The Cutting of the Cable

WHILE Osberne ate, two or three came to learn what adventures he had, and how things were on board the *San Antonio,* and by what means he had escaped. After he had told them all, how the Indians had received him, and how and why he came back to the fleet, and how he had deserted, he heard the news of what had passed on the ships, and it did not seem possible that so much could have happened on one day.

"The worst of it is that all your friends, Fernandez and Diaz and Rodriguez are in irons," said a bright-eyed page. "I heard that told to Barbosa when we went, on orders, to find out how far the mutiny had reached. A priest, Father Pedro, told us."

75

" And what of Lorriaga? " asked Osberne. " There for you was a man with a heart like a lion. You should have seen him fly at Quesada. But I saw him wounded at the moment I fell overboard with those two."

" Lorriaga, poor fellow, is at the point of death, and the priest sits with him, waiting for the end," was the answer. " Not only Quesada, but also his servant Molino stabbed the Basque. A merrier soul than he for a companion man could not want."

Hearing that, Osberne's heart turned cold, for he felt that in swimming away to shore he had deserted his companion, so said something of the sort.

" Do not take that too much to heart," said Hans. " As matters ran you would have been a mad fool to climb back on the ship and be stabbed, or have your throat cut. You would surely have been dead. As things are, you may help them yet."

" And I shall," declared Osberne. " But how are the men? Do they stand with Quesada? "

" Now look at it," said the page. " How should it matter to the men who is master? If the flag of one captain, or the flag of another flies, the men's days will be days of hardship, so they do not care. These fights are the fights of captains. The men gain nothing by them. On the *San Antonio* they made Juan Sebastian del Cano captain. What did he do, think you, to gain the good will of the men? "

" Promised them much, I suppose," said Osberne.

" Promised them easy times, they say. Then he opened the stores and gave everybody a feast and a full belly. So there they were, all day, eating and drinking and singing, and now and then firing a bombard."

Osberne pushed aside his platter and wiped his fingers by running them through his hair. "So the matter stands now that the mutineers have the *San Antonio,* and the Magellan men have the other four ships. One against four."

"You reckon wrong, Osberne," said the page. "It is three mutinied ships against two. Mendoza is captain of the *Victoria* and he is against Magellan, being a Spaniard. The *Concepcion* flies the flag of Spain, and has hauled down the admiral's banner. Yesterday Magellan sent the boats to all the ships to find out where they stood. I was in one of them. We did not go near, but hailed them from a distance. 'Who are ye for?' we asked, and back came the answer, 'For the king and ourselves!'"

"Can the matter be patched up, think you, Hans, or will the fleet split, some going back, some going on?" asked Osberne.

"The whole thing is patch upon patch, and patch upon patch is beggary," said Hans.

"But all fights end in death or talk," said Osberne. "The captains should meet together and come to an end for order's sake."

"Put all these captains in a bag and shake them, and out will come a rascal," said Hans. "They know that, therefore they do not trust one another. Magellan wants a meeting on board the *Trinidad,* but the others suspect a trap and will not agree. The others want a meeting on board the *San Antonio,* but Magellan and Serrao suspect a trap and will not go. There the matter stands, neither side giving way. They use honeyed words, but in honeyed words treason hides. The sweet words are the bait, and well they all know that it is easy to get into a trap but hard to get out. There was the trap that Magellan set for Cartagena. That has not been forgotten."

"It sickens me, all this disorder," said the page. "I think it would be better to go on shore and live with the Indians. I am minded to do so."

"Anything would be better than to stay cooped up here," said a sailor.

"But cooping time is done," bawled Andrew, who had entered a moment before. "Here is Barbosa calling for men to row the boats and we are left guessing the why of it. You, Osberne, had better busy yourself. All is at sixes and sevens, with no order anywhere. Hans and you must come in the long boat with Barbosa."

"What is the other boat?" asked the page.

"The skiff," said Andrew.

"Who takes charge?"

"Espinosa."

"Then," said the page, "I want none of that."

"It is arranged," said Andrew. "Five men go with that, all of them secretly armed."

"Then we can put two and two together," said the page. "I know that Magellan and Espinosa have talked of sending a letter to Mendoza of the *Victoria*. I heard something of it while I worked in the admiral's cabin. But they whispered and sent me out. That was just before I came in to talk with Osberne."

They said much of that while they were getting themselves ready, but on deck they said no more. There stood Barbosa, big and burly, on the side of the ship where his boat was fastened. On the other side stood Espinosa, a man small, black of chin, crooked of mouth, and talking, as was his habit, of his high honor. "I stand for right," he said. "I am for open dealing." "I cannot stain my honor," and much more of the same sort.

" Butter mouth and fox heart," said Hans. " The cross on his breast and the devil in his heart."

" Fifteen men in my boat! " shouted Barbosa. " Silva will give each man a dagger as he goes overboard. You shall be told what to do when the time comes. For the present, Andrew, you will pick your rowers. We pull to the *Victoria.* The skiff goes to the larboard side and we to the starboard. No man boards until the word is given."

So down to the long boat they went, Osberne at the bow with orders to handle the boat hook when they came alongside the *Victoria,* and Hans with a boat hook at the stern, while Andrew steered.

" Give way men! " ordered Barbosa, and they pulled lustily, the skiff with Espinosa and his five armed men keeping alongside. And no sooner did Osberne feel the lift of the wave, and hear the splash of water against boat side, and know that he was away from quarreling men, when he felt heartened and lifted up.

So they came to the *Victoria* and there the men took in their oars and lay alongside, while Osberne and Hans hooked their boat hooks to the ship. Thus, standing, they saw all that went forward on the deck.

Barbosa stood up and called, " Captain Mendoza, we come with a peaceful message."

Then Mendoza walked to the side of the ship and looked down into the boat, nodding kindly at the men.

" Shall they lift their hands to show there are no weapons? " asked Barbosa.

" There is no need of that," answered Mendoza, at which Osberne felt the blood run to his face and had a mind to call out for the captain to beware of treachery.

" Barbosa," said Captain Mendoza, " this is a silly business.

You are a sensible man and must see that all may yet go well. We ask no more than that Magellan shall consult with us, not to the end that we may cross him, or be no-sayers, but that we shall see the why and how of things. I am for peace and there need be no blustering and masterful work. A good general talks with his captains, consults with them too, and out of many heads comes wisdom. You must say these things to your kinsman Magellan."

"I will, Captain," said Barbosa, heartily.

"Then give your message," said the captain, who, it was clear, did not dream of treachery.

Hearing all that, Osberne felt full of shame to be in the boat where a traitor and a liar held command. "At least I shall be fair," he said, to himself, and secretly dropped the dagger that had been given him into the sea.

"I have no message," said Barbosa, "but I come as escort. It is Espinosa who carries the letter."

"Thank you," said the captain, and reached out and shook Barbosa by the hand. Then he went to the other side of the ship.

Mendoza looked over the side, not standing too near, and said, "Espinosa, what is it now?"

"I am bearer of a letter asking you to come with us to the flagship to talk with the admiral," answered Espinosa.

"Let me see your letter," said Mendoza.

"Have I safe conduct to come aboard?" asked Espinosa. "Those who bring peace should stand close together as friends do. Not talk from a distance."

"Do you suppose me a coward to take advantage of an unarmed man, Espinosa?" asked the captain.

As he said that, Mendoza threw out his open hands to show

that he had no weapon, then ordered his sailors to stand back
so that Espinosa might have a clear space.

"Thank you, Captain," said Espinosa, and stepped on to the
deck, but called to his five men, saying, "Come men. Here we
have fair treatment. Clean hands and honor. All shall be
fair and open."

Osberne, standing and holding his boat hook, heard and saw
all that, and felt glad that all was going well. But what he
saw next sickened him. For Mendoza took the letter and
turned a little to get the sunlight on the paper, so that he had
his back to Espinosa. Then, like a tiger, the false Espinosa
leaped at the captain and struck him in the neck with his
dagger. The wounded man wheeled, a look of surprise in his
eyes, and though the blood spurted out and stained his cloak,
he thrust out a hand and caught at the traitor's arm which was
upraised for a second stroke. But the five armed men threw
themselves on the wounded man and stabbed, every one of
them most furiously, in body and in face, so that Mendoza fell
on deck a dead man.

"Kill the false fellows!" roared a sailor, and the men came
rushing down the deck, but Espinosa and his men retreated to
the side of the ship where lay Barbosa. Then Barbosa called
out, "On deck!" and leaped to the *Victoria's* deck followed by
ten of his men, all of them ready and around.

"More shameful treachery I never saw," cried Andrew. "I
will have no hand in it."

"Sinful man as I am, I never saw worse falseness," cried
Hans.

Osberne felt too sick to look, and sank back in the boat sore
at heart and ashamed. His heart seemed to stand still. At that
moment the land of Patagonia with its Indians seemed a haven

most desirable, so he cried out to Andrew, as soon as he could find heart to say a word, "Let us go away and ashore out of it. It sickens me."

"Alas!" said Andrew. "We are sworn to a duty and may yet bring order out of this. These masters of ours are all mired in the same muck. So what can a man do but the work nearest?"

By then Barbosa had ordered Magellan's flag to be run to the masthead. But there were some of the *Victoria's* men who burning with fierce revenge had been below to get pikes and swords, and they came shouting and threatening and calling for blood. And lined along the deck were the men with Barbosa and the five with Espinosa, so that it looked as if blood would flow. Seeing that and fearing what might come, Andrew leaped to the deck and ran between the two parties with his arms flung out, crying, "Men! Men! Why spill more blood? Hold your hands! This is the fight of the masters and not of the men!" Also Osberne, full of bitter anger and shame, shouted out from where he stood, begging the men to do no killing. Some of the *Victoria's* men joined in and so the trouble seemed stayed. But two men went on their knees beside the dead body of Mendoza, weeping and lifting up and down their clasped hands in an agony of grief. "Blood for blood!" one of them cried, and two or three others took up the cry, "Blood for blood!" Thereupon Hans climbed on deck and tied the boat, after which he and Osberne, helped by two men of the *Victoria,* lifted the body of Mendoza and carried it to the after-deck where they reverently crossed the hands on the breast and laid a sword under them, then draped a flag over the dead man.

"Up anchor!" shouted Barbosa, and while some men ran

ESPINOSA

·FOX·FACE·

to do that others put sail on the ship, so under the light wind
they dropped down to the mouth of the harbor and there anchored. Next the *Trinidad* sailed near to the same place and
anchored, and then the little *Santiago* did the same. Thus the
three ships bottled up the harbor so that neither the *San Antonio* nor the *Concepcion* could get out except by fighting a
way through.

For the rest of that day there was hot work to do, especially
for the gunners. Darts, lances, arrows and even great stones
were set here and there about the decks and in the tops. Andrew and Hans worked hard getting ready the bombards and
training them; and the boys brought cannon balls, and set
culverins, and fetched gunpowder, making all ready. Arquebuses were set up. Javelins and boarding pikes and swords
were set in handy places on the decks of the three ships. And
about and about walked Magellan and Espinosa, dressed in
armor.

" How sick I am of all this," said the English gunner. " Here
we have a giant's work to do, getting round the world, but must
needs spill one another's blood before we are well started.
How can a thing be well done when nothing but hate abounds?
Deeds worth doing should be done in good fellowship."

"Forgive us our trespasses, indeed," said Hans. " It is a
sorry business. There are good fellows on the other ships, and
here our masters set us to killing our own friends. Saw ever
man greater foolishness, I ask? "

They were talking loud because of the noise of rolling cannon balls, and the clash of weapons, calling to one another
across the deck.

"For me it is as if I swam from hell to heaven what time I
swam ashore from the *San Antonio*," said Osberne, talking

to both Hans and Andrew. "But coming from the land to this *Trinidad,* I swam from heaven to hell. My next swim, I trust, shall be to heaven again."

"A good swimmer," said a voice, and, looking up, Osberne saw the fox-face of Espinosa. "This time you shall swim from one hell to another, since these ships are hell to you."

Osberne stood up and could have bitten off his tongue for what it had said.

"How long, think you, would it take you to swim to the *San Antonio* before the tide commenced to run out?" asked fox-face Espinosa.

At first Osberne did not answer, because he was wondering what it might mean.

"Ha! Then there is a coward's heart perhaps in this deserter," said Espinosa, taking the silence for fear. At that taunt Osberne's body stiffened and his fists closed tight. He thought that if he had a quarterstaff and stood on Portsdown green with this fellow, both of them matched in even fight, then the ruffian would sing another tune. But he answered, "I could swim the distance in a half an hour, perhaps."

The crooked smile that every man hated to see came across Espinosa's face. "Tell me," he said, "why came ye on this voyage?"

"To see how places are," answered Osberne. "Also to know adventure. And to go round the world."

"Then you shall see things. You shall do what has not been done before. You shall go round the world too, my lad. But we may never get on our way if things go as they are. The *San Antonio* must be brought out and you shall do it."

"Send me on no such errands as that we had with the *Victoria,*" said Osberne. "I will die sooner than play traitor."

"Ah! That took brains, my lad," said Espinosa. "This takes muscle. But hold your tongue now. Put a stout heart to a steep hill. Here is your work for the good of the fleet and the making of order. You shall swim to the *San Antonio*. If you board her you are lost because they will give you the rope as a deserter. If you come back to any of these loyal ships without doing that which you are sent to do, then again you shall have the rope as a worthless fellow. If you swim to land you are a coward and one who will not stay with his friends, so then also it is the rope for you. So do this. Here is a sharp knife which you must put in your belt. You shall swim to the *San Antonio* and cut the anchor cable, which is not chain like ours, for they have lost the chain they had. Make a good job of it. Being loose the *San Antonio* will drift out with the tide and we shall do the rest. If you drown then you are at an end. But the better thing will be for you to hang on by rudder or rope and find us again."

"By all the saints, you give the lad too great a task," said Andrew. "I offer to do it if it must be done."

"Or I," said Hans.

"Or I," said a page.

Espinosa turned on the last speaker savagely and gave him a blow that sent him reeling. "That is your answer," he said.

"And is our answer to be of that sort?" asked Andrew angrily, "because such answers call for other answers of heavier kind." There was a light in the gunner's eye that did not please Espinosa, so he stepped back a little.

"You gunners have your work," said he. "Your duty is with your guns. This lad has already been a deserter in time of battle when he swam ashore. What he may have engaged in on board the *San Antonio* I know not, but, doubtless, there were deeds. I know not. He may have been false with guards. I say I know not. He may have opened cabins. Again I know not. But if he did any of those things he has earned the rope or the ax. Doing this, in the matter of the swim, he shall have our good wishes and forgiveness. But he may be a coward and afraid of the work. In that case there is the rope or the ax should he refuse. Or he may play false and swim ashore so that the plans we have planned may be brought to naught. In that case it may be that the head of his friend, let us say Hans, might answer for his desertion. It is a hard case."

Espinosa looked sideways as a fox does.

"By all the saints," began Hans, standing up, but Andrew set a hand on his arm and stopped him.

"Let the lad manage his affair," said Andrew. "He will do well enough."

"Give me the knife," said Osberne, and Espinosa threw it on the ground. Then he stepped back a pace, as if in fear.

Osberne picked up the knife, tested its edge with his thumb, then stuck it in his belt. Next he shook hands with Hans and Andrew and also with the page, bidding them good-bye as he did so.

"Is there no word of farewell for me?" asked Espinosa.

"Yes. A greater rogue and liar I never saw," answered Osberne, and in one voice Hans and Andrew said, "Well spoken."

With that Osberne ran to the side, waved once more to his friends, then dived into the water, hitting it clean and straight, and when he came up blew the water out of his nose and struck out.

It was no light job to swim in so chill a sea, but there was comfort in being away from all that noise and blood and hate. At times, as he swam, he thought of Ato, his Indian friend, and how, if he swam ashore he might find him and enjoy the peace of the life the Indian led. But the thought of his sea companions came and he put the other aside. Once he got tangled in the long, snaky seaweed that got about his legs like ropes, but he cut himself adrift with the knife. He came safely to the ship, and as he swam alongside to the bows he could hear the men on board talking and laughing. Strangely kind all the while he felt toward Lorriaga on his deathbed, and to those others he knew, with whom he had fought.

The cutting of the cable took a long time for he had to hold with one hand and saw far above his head with the other at a place where the thick rope was dry, but when he had almost done, or so nearly done that the strands began to break of themselves under the weight, he slid into the water then swam sternwards and hung on to the rudder. There because of the counter that overhung he could not be seen from the deck.

Soon a great hubbub arose on the ship.

" We are adrift! " shouted one.

" Get way on the ship," he heard another say.

" We must surely run ashore," a third cried.

Looking up he saw the glare of torches, and the noise of men's voices grew greater. By the way the sea had ceased to ripple against the side of the ship he knew that things had gone well and that the tide was carrying the *San Antonio* to the mouth of the bay where the three ships lay. Presently he could not bring himself to hang there any longer in the dark, seeing nothing and knowing nothing, but, for very curiosity's sake must climb up and look over the deck, though to do so might be full of danger. So up the rudder-post he went, climbing by toes and fingers, hanging like a cat, taking every crack and cranny for a toehold, until he could see over the bulwarks.

By the light of torches he saw Gaspar Quesada, in armor and carrying a lance and shield. He was like a man mad, calling and threatening, and sometimes striking men. But the sailors seemed in no mood to fight, nor to hoist a sail, nor to do anything. They stood in sullen groups, whispering together.

"For the king! For the king!" Quesada shouted. "Will you raise no hand against this upstart Magellan? Are you men or cowardly dogs?"

Then he fell to cursing.

One man stepped forward, a common sailor, and Osberne in his hiding-place heard him shout, "Jackanapes of a captain! What matters it to us under which flag we sail? It is nothing but blows and hard fare and misery. For me the captains may fight until they are all killed. We who do the work shall go on our own ways."

So arose a hubbub with every man talking and gathered about those who held torches. And it came to Osberne that with good luck, and every one so engaged, he might slip down to the cabin where Lorriaga lay, knowing the corners of that ship as he did; but he knew that he would have to be quick. So he slid over to the deck and across it in the shade of the little deck house, then ran down the companion-way, and to the cabin. But when he looked in at the cabin he saw, by the light of the lantern, Lorriaga lying on the cot and the priest on his knees by his side. He thought his companion dead, until he saw the heaving chest. Then, "Forgive me," Osberne said to the priest, and touched the sick man's hand. Lorriaga opened his eyes and looked up, not at all surprised. The priest made the sign of the cross and said nothing.

"How go things, lad?" asked Lorrigia, but Osberne could find no words.

When the sick man spoke again, after a little while, he said, in a very weak voice, " Life need not have all this ugly riot, lad. The adventure has been good, but the greed of men for place turns good into bad. It has brought all this sorrow and pain." His words came slow and far between. " Osberne, there is this. As I am a sinful man, the best things in the world are order and friendship. I have thought the world was made for our delight. But our masters turn us to destroy and . . . there is no need . . ."

Osberne waited, but the sick man could say no more. Then the priest signed to the lad to be gone, and he went. Out on deck things had changed. There was no need for him to hide in shadows, for excited men were running every way, trying to find hiding-places for themselves, knowing that the ship drifted to a stern enemy.

But suddenly he remembered the others who had fought with Lorriaga, so he ran back to the cabin and spoke to the priest.

" Father Pedro," he said, " the ship drifts to the bay because I have cut the rope. I would not be traitor to my friends. The other ships make ready to fire as this one draws near, and much blood may be shed. Will you go on deck and pray the men to stay their hands? Tell them to do nothing. Let the masters fight if they will, but let the men stand aside. I promise you that those on the other ships will not fire if no gun is fired from this deck. The gunners seek no blood. In the name of God I pray this."

" It is well, my son," said the priest. " What man can do I shall do." So he went.

Then Osberne ran along the dark way where he had run before when he opened the cabin, until he came to the cell where the prisoners were kept, and through the grating he saw them, not chained but loose, though the door was locked. At his greeting they started to their feet and began talking.

" The key of the door," he said. " Who keeps the key? Tell me quick. For there may be killing and there may be fire. Free, you may do something, though I know not what."

" Molino, the servant of Quesada keeps the key," one of them answered; and off went Osberne to find him. In the dark and confusion no man heeded another, so Osberne asked this one and that, and at last a ship's boy said that he had seen him go to Quesada's cabin. Down Osberne went then and found the door shut but unlocked, so he softly opened it. And there was Molino on his hands and knees, at an open box, and, on the floor beside it, little heaps of money. But for gold and silver Osberne had no thought. With a leap he was on the man, forcing him backwards until he pinned him to the floor, Osberne's knees holding down Molino's arms, his left hand at his throat, his right hand feeling for the key at chest and at girdle.

" I give up the money! I give up the money! " gasped Molino, his eyes staring with terror.

" I care nothing for the money," answered Osberne, " but it is death to you if you do not open the prison cell."

Easier victory man could not have had, for the fellow craved release, and wept in shameful manner. " Beat me not," he said, " let me rise." And being freed, " Come," said he, then led the way to the cell. So the door was unlocked and the prisoners having been released, Molino was locked up in their place and they left him beating with open hands on the bars and crying out, but sometimes cursing. But Osberne would not let the released men go until he made them promise to do what they could to prevent the men from fighting.

"Nor will that be hard," said one of them, "for the men would not fight did not the masters stir them up. As for us, we have no quarrel with them. They are our shipmates and we have suffered together."

So Osberne went on the deck again and there saw that the *San Antonio* had drawn near to the three ships that guarded the mouth of the bay. He could see the torches, and looking more closely, the men like shadows, and, because he knew where they were, the arms that had been set up. On the *San Antonio* Captain Quesada stormed up and down, calling on the men to take sword and pike, and fight, but others went about among the men, and with them the priest, begging them for their own sakes and for the sakes of their fellows to lift no hand. Looking to the *Trinidad,* Osberne saw Andrew and Hans standing by their guns. Then, as the ships drew nearer, the *San Antonio* drifting broadside on, Osberne leaped into the sea and struck out for the *Trinidad,* swimming strongly so as not to be drawn between the ships by the water and so crushed to death. And before he had touched the ship's side he heard two bombards roar, but he knew that neither Andrew nor Hans were firing at the other ships, but wide of the mark. Hand over hand he went up the cable and swung himself aboard over the bows, then ran among the men.

"The men of the *San Antonio* do not want to shed blood," he cried again and again. "Hold your hands! Let the captains fight among themselves." More especially he begged the archers not to shoot.

As the ships touched, grappling irons were thrown out and the *San Antonio* was held. But not a shot was fired, nor did the men give any show of fight, but stood with folded arms. Gladly enough though did men from both ships run forward to arrest Captain Quesada who showed no valiant bearing whatever, but called on men to rescue him. But Juan de Cartagena would suffer no man to touch him. Alone he stepped up to Magellan and offered him his sword.

"I have played and lost," he said, in a voice that half the ship could hear. "You have my word that I will not try to escape. And I offer the surrender of the *Concepcion*. The men have no stomach for fighting so captains are at an end."

Then he walked down the deck and sat on the water cask with his arms folded.

And thus ended the mutiny in which no man was killed nor any wounded. But it did not end the revenge.

No man knew what kind of trial was held. All that could be known was that Magellan, and Espinosa, and Barbosa, and Serrao shut themselves up in a cabin with guards outside the door. The prisoners were in their cells and Juan de Cartagena was locked in his cabin.

Presently the door opened and the four judges came out, dressed in their breastplates and with neck pieces and greaves, and carrying swords and shields.

Then out stepped a herald who blew a trumpet and said, "The masters of the fleet have judged those who would have betrayed us and this is the punishment. Captain Quesada is deprived of his command. He will be taken ashore where his head will be struck off, and his body cut into four pieces and the quarters stuck upon poles. He who was Captain Mendoza, but who was killed by our good friend and servant Espinosa —"

Here some one shouted out, "Espinosa the Judas! Magellan paid him money to do the foul deed."

Then Magellan stepped forward and his face was dark with

anger. "If any will name the name of the man who called out, he shall be rewarded and the caller hanged at the yardarm."

But no one spoke.

"Our good friend and servant Espinosa," went on the herald, "this Mendoza's body shall be taken ashore and there quartered and the four pieces hung on poles."

"Again a voice cried out, saying, "And where shall Espinosa be hanged?"

Another cried, "Let him be hanged side by side with Magellan."

"Another cry such as that and the gunners shall fire into the crowd," roared Magellan.

The herald went on. "Forty others have been found guilty of treason but we pardon them if they carry themselves well."

Again a voice cried out, "Come now and take the forty."

"As for Juan de Cartagena," cried the herald, "he has given his word that he will attempt no escape. So him we leave for a time. Know all men that by the Titulo de Capitanes, given by the king, Ferdinand Magellan was granted power of rope and knife over every person in the armada."

So Quesada and Molino went ashore, and in the boat lay the body of Mendoza, but not a man in the fleet could be found who would act as executioner, and when the time came the foul work had to be done by Molino and Espinosa.

CHAPTER V

"Ma-ee-ya, Ota-bben!"

ALL THAT winter every one worked hard, patching up the ships, cleaning and trimming, doing a thousand and one things. In the open air, with good food in plenty and with regular sleep the men grew strong and happy, their skins became tanned and their eyes bright. But matters did not promise to go so well at the beginning. Indeed there seemed likely to be another outbreak because the food was weighed out and only a little given to each man. As for

talking the matter over with the officers, there seemed small
chance of that because between master and men lay a wide
gulf. Magellan and Espinosa and one or two others walked
apart from the men. Then, when four chosen by the rest of
the men went to the cabin to talk to Magellan about the food,
they were met by Espinosa who smiled his crooked smile and
told them that he would attend to such matters.

So the four went back to their fellows and told what there
was to tell and for a while there were mutterings and
grumblings.

" It is folly," said Osberne, " for us to go hungry when here
is a land, as I well know, in which a man may have all that he
wants to eat and more. With my bow and arrow I will bring
back enough in a day for a ship. Or going with the Indians,
who are a good folk, I shall bring back enough for the fleet.
But the Indians are a simple folk and may not be treated ill.
I am with them more than with our captains, to say truth."

" But a man cannot get away into the country without being
sent," said a page. " That would be desertion and would mean
the rope."

Osberne said, " Then I shall see Magellan and get past this
Espinosa, or else be a badly beaten fellow."

" And then you will have to beware of the smoldering wrath
of Fox-face," said Manuel the page.

As it fell out, Osberne's chance came early, for that day being Sunday they left off work sooner than usual, and Osberne
and Andrew fell to playing at quarterstaff on the deck of the
Trinidad. As the blows sounded much worse than they were,
for both players knew how to play and warded off the dangerous hits, but laid heavily enough on to leather-guarded shoulders and backs, the other men gathered round looking on, won-

dering much at the seeming roughness of the sport, that not being a Spanish play. Presently both Magellan and Barbosa stopped to look, and then Espinosa came and joined them. Soon the sailors began calling out, as men will, some for Andrew and some for Osberne. But loudest of all among them was Espinosa, not because he loved the sport but because to see pain suffered gave him great joy, as is the case with some.

" Crack his head! " he cried at one time. Then at another, " Lay on more lustily! " and again, " Had I the staff I would have made the blood flow."

Presently Andrew lifted his hand to stay Osberne, then said, " It is stark folly for me to play quarterstaff when there is one here who, by his words, knows the game so much better," and looked at Espinosa.

And Magellan, being in one of his happy moods, said, " You hear that, Espinosa? How about it? "

" In my day I played thus with the Germans, but not for many years," answered Espinosa. " But I remember many a trick."

" Then take the staff and play against one of these," said Magellan, hearing which Espinosa smiled foolishly.

" Some of these days I will do so," he said. " But my arm is not so strong as it was in its prime. In those days I fed much on meat and fish and fowl, as do the English and the Germans. Now, when we must needs pinch and trim, my muscle is not what it was."

" Any excuse will serve when one has not a mind to do a thing, as we say in Portugal," said Magellan.

" This is a new side to the admiral," whispered Andrew to Hans.

Then a thought came to Osberne and he lifted his hand, as a

boy at school does, and as was the habit on the fleet when a
man would speak to an officer. But Espinosa would not see the
sign, thinking that it might mean some impudent offer with
the quarterstaff.

" What it is? " asked Magellan of Osberne, a little sternly
because of the pride of place in him.

" My Admiral," said Osberne, " I ask now the forgiveness
that was promised me when I swam to the *San Antonio.*"

" Who made such promise? " asked Magellan, coldly.

But Osberne would not take notice of his coldness. " The
constable Espinosa, Captain-general."

Thereupon Magellan turned to Espinosa and asked him
what the promise was.

" I said something. This lad had deserted," answered
Espinosa.

Magellan frowned. " A deserter! That is not to be forgiven.
Did you go to my Spanish enemies? " he asked.

In his inmost mind Osberne found himself somewhat amazed
that he felt no fear at all, though friends about him were whispering to him to bridle his tongue.

" No, Captain-general," he said. " I went with the Indians
on shore."

" Go on," commanded Magellan. " I am told that they are
giants."

" It is a long story," answered Osberne. " Wilt thou hear it
in quiet? "

" That is no way to talk to the Captain-general," said Espinosa.

" Yet thus I talked to Sir Robert, who is a great lord and the
owner of a ship and a castle in England," answered Osberne.

Then Magellan slowly stepped forward, and those about Os-

berne drew back leaving a wide space for the two, though
Andrew stayed near. The admiral laid a hand on Osberne's
shoulder, not lightly, but in the manner of one who would
show another his muscle. He gripped with a strong grip, but
Osberne flinched not at all, but rather stood the straighter. It
came to Osberne's mind that the admiral was full of suspicion,
so the lad said, " I have no weapons, neither have I any enmity
in me."

" Come thou to the forecastle and tell me what thou hast
seen," said Magellan. " It may be that there are some in this
fleet who can talk straightly and plan no black mischief. You
may let us be in peace, Espinosa."

So Magellan led the way to a quiet place on the forecastle
and sat on a box, and, without being told to do so, Osberne
squatted on the deck with his legs crossed and his hands holding his ankles, as he had done many a time when talking to
Sir Robert. As soon as they were seated, Espinosa came and
whispered to Magellan, " May not there be some new trap
here? Would a guard be well?'"

" Leave me," said Magellan. " Here to-day I am a happy
man for a little while. I have found one not afraid to talk
straight. He may tell me things that hurt, it is true, but truth
hurts often. If I like not what I hear, it may be because it is
something I should hear. If thou hast no other errand, then
begone for a while."

So Espinosa left them together, but not willingly.

" Talk now as you did to your great lord," commanded
Magellan.

Then Osberne told about his day on the land with Ato, and
presently as he went on he put aside all that outward form and
falseness of the fleet by which men talked to their officers as

MAGELLAN HEARS OSBERNES STORY

though they were gods. He talked as he was used to talk to
Sir Robert when they were hunting or fishing, what time
he would say that this or that should be done. And Sir
Robert had heard, and acted, knowing how Osberne knew the
way of the field and the wild creatures. Osberne felt much at
ease.

"You must know, Admiral," he said in ending, "a man in
power often has about him lying tongues. Also he may see
with crooked eyes when he does not see for himself. He may
act in silly fashion when he has a fool or a rascal for adviser."

"And have I then listened to lying tongues, and have I seen
with crooked eyes, and have I acted in silly fashion because a
fool sat at my right hand?" asked Magellan.

"As to the last we act in silly fashion even now," answered
Osberne. "Four men went to see you about food, but they
saw only Espinosa who sent them away. Doubtless you knew
nothing of that."

"Go on. I am not here to confess but to hear," said Magellan.
"There must be caution, for a long voyage lies ahead."

"Caution, yes. Folly, no. And it is folly to work on short
commons when we are in a land of more food than Spain or
England. I tell you, Captain-general, we can live like fighting-
cocks."

"But it is a desert land, I am told," said Magellan.

"And I say it is no desert," answered Osberne. "If there
are Indian people, then Indians must eat. Food not being
plentiful they would go elsewhere. Give me leave to be ashore
two days and I shall bring down to the ships food for a ban-
quet for a king. And let the men fish in the bay. There is no
need to stint."

"Would you go alone?" asked Magellan.

" Alone if you wish. With two good companions, or three, if you give me leave later on."

" And you ask nothing? No office? No reward? "

" Nothing, sir." But no sooner had the word passed his lips than he raised his hand.

" Well, what now? " asked Magellan.

" I would have your word that if I come with Indians down to the ships then there shall be no ill-treatment of them."

" That is fair enough," said Magellan, rising from his seat. So Osberne stood up. For a little while Magellan looked out to sea, somewhat sadly, Osberne thought. Then he said, " Boy, it has been good to hear straight talk. Now tell me one thing, if an answer leaps to your lips; if not, then say nothing."

" I will answer if it has nothing to do with my friends," said Osberne, then added, " nor with what may be said among us."

" Nothing of that sort, boy," answered Magellan. " It is this. In what, think you, am I fortunate and in what unfortunate? "

" As I see it you are fortunate in being head of this adventure. You are most unfortunate in having no friend," answered Osberne.

" You hit the mark," said Magellan. " You should make a good hunter. So try your fortune for two days. You are free for that time and we shall see what food you bring us." Then he arose and went somewhat painfully down the deck because of his old wound which gave him twinges if he sat long.

So it came about that Osberne again fared forth into Patagonia, not walking cautiously as before, but often running because he was all on fire to meet Ato. He carried his bow, a sheaf of good arrows, and a staff. And the way was pleasant for the sun shone in a clear sky and a brisk wind brought

tingling warmth to his skin. And there were little hills, and
great hills beyond, and a stream by which he rested. Once he
saw a great flock of the yellow and white animals like those
that the Indians had tamed, but these were wild and sped over
the land with such swiftness and lightness that they seemed
not to touch the earth. Up from grassy places rose great flocks
of wild ducks and geese, and once he stood stock-still to watch
a great bird like an eagle, but much larger, that hung in the
air, wheeled and then swept up against the wind without moving a wing. At another time a red-breasted bird like a great
living flame flew up, and he knew it for a flamingo. Hawks
too he saw, and doves, and crested birds that screamed. And
there were swift ostriches, and partridges, and a thousand chat-
tering birds with long tails most beautiful to see. But all that
day he saw no sign of man until gloaming. Then, as he stood
on a low hill and looked up and down over the sea of grass,
he saw, far off, a light blue smoke. So down the valley he went,
southward, and came to a noisy stream, but by that time it was
dark and he could not see the smoke, nor did he know the way
in which the fire lay. Thereupon he lay down to wait for the
light of morning, finding much to make him laugh in the
strange noises of night birds and strange insects.

When he woke in the morning, opening his eyes and not
stirring, what was his surprise to see Ato, very upright, very
still, standing near. He held a long spear with its point stuck
in the ground. So Osberne fell a-thinking that the Indian must
have come there some time before, while he was in that deep
sleep, and had watched over him. Proud as any knight the
Indian seemed, with a pleasant look upon his face, and a tall
feather in his hair, and a fur cloak hanging from his shoulders
and fastened with a thong, but no other dress except a kind of

cloth about his loins, for in that fashion all the Indians were dressed.

Then Osberne spoke, and leaped to his feet, crying, "Ha! Ato! By all the saints I am glad to see thee."

With a leap Ato was across the stream, and the two lads greeted one another with right hands on left shoulders and looking into one another's eyes, and Ato said something which the other did not understand but took to mean, "I began to fear you would not come again." For that was the fashion of their talk, one saying something and the other guessing it to mean this or that, but as all was said in friendliness it did not greatly matter whether the guess was right or wrong.

Then Ato said something, and while saying pointed and traced a line across the country from the bay to the place where they stood, then, with his left hand traced another line from the hills to where they stood. Osberne took it to mean that the Indian had seen him running on the day before and himself had run to meet him. Then Osberne stood awhile with knitted brows, wondering how he would make known to Ato that he came to hunt meat for the ships and needed help, for he had not thought of the difference in tongues when he talked with Magellan. So he began by pointing to his mouth and making signs of eating, and at once Ato turned about and took from where it lay a bag, and brought out cooked meat, and part of a wild duck, which he salted and gave to Osberne, who attacked it with good appetite. While he filled himself, the Indian said, over and over again, with a smile, "Ma-ee-ya, Ota-bben! Ma-ee-ya!" which Osberne took to mean, "Welcome, Osberne! Welcome!" and Osberne in his turn said, "Ma-ee-ya, Ato! Ma-ee-ya!" which seemed to please the Indian, so all promised well. But still Osberne wondered how he might make all his

wants known, the more because of the time being short; and
with two days given him one had already gone.

At last a thought came.

There was a place in the stream where the water flowed
into a quiet spot making a pool, and, scraping the gravel a
little, Osberne formed it into the shape of the bay where the five
ships lay. At first Ato seemed to wonder, but soon came to understand. Next Osberne took five leaves and put them in the
water near to two rocks that in his mind stood for the islands
in the bay, then blew them about a little to show that they stood
for the ships. Taking a smaller leaf he laid in it a little twig
and blew the leaf to land, after leaving the twig on the shore,
then blew it back again to the leaf that stood for a ship. Osberne saw a smile come to Ato's face when Osberne took the
twig and touched his own breast with it, to show that it stood
for him; then he returned it to the ground. After that he took
another twig and touched Ato on the breast with it, then put
that twig far away on a hillock. Next, he moved the two twigs
that stood for Osberne and Ato, one towards another, then laid
one on the ground and stood the other in the ground by its
side, and he knew that Ato understood then, because the Indian said in two different voices, " Ma-ee-ya, Ota-bben! " and
" Ma-ee-ya, Ato! " Next Ato took the two twigs between his
finger and thumb and moved them away from the direction of
the water so that Osberne knew that it was in his friend's mind
that they should go away into the hills. But Osberne shook
his head, then pondered awhile wondering how he might carry
his message to the other, and he soon found a way. Taking the
twig that stood for Ato, he moved it a little way up the bank
and to a place where other twigs were, then stuck many of
them upright in the ground.

" Cume! Cume! " cried Ato, which Osberne took to mean
" Good! Good! "

Next Osberne took other twigs and laid them on the five
leaves, that were ships, meaning that there were men beset by
famine and weak. After that, he stuck tiny pieces of food, on
the upright twigs that were Osberne and Ato, then marched the
twigs with the food down to the side of the pool. After that
taking the twigs from the leaves, he carried them to the water-
side and made the twigs with the food deliver the meat to the
twigs that he had taken from the leaves, and ended by putting
the meat on the five leaves.

At that Ato commenced to laugh for pure joy, laughed so
much indeed that he rolled on the ground, then got to his feet
and danced about, then pushed the five leaves down the stream
gently, all loaded with twigs and meat, and at the end took the
two twigs that stood for himself and for Osberne and marched
them up the bank. So Osberne understood that as meaning
that he would be welcome to stay with the Indians if he wished
to let the fleet sail away. But he would make no promise to
that end.

" That shall be seen to, Ato," he said, though his heart
thumped against his ribs as he thought of the clean life of the
land and how he loved it more than all that hatred and bloodshed on the fleet.

So they went, the two of them, out of the little valley and
over a low-lying hill, and came to the Indian camp of a dozen
tents, and close by a few of the graceful animals the size of an
ass which Osberne came to know as guanacos. There were
young men there, and boys playing, and old men working
with skins and hides and feathers, and women at cooking and
seeing to weapons, all of them as merry and busy as bees in

spring. They greeted Osberne and Ato pleasantly, and one of
the boys in play, as boys everywhere might do, threw a rope in
such a way that the noose fell about Osberne's chest so that
his arms would be fast bound to his sides had he run. So he
stood still, amazed at the skill of the boy, for he had never seen
that sort of clever work before. But not so Ato, who caught
the boy and gave him a little clout, and seemed severe. Another
man, who seemed to be a head-man, as if in sudden but short-
lived anger, took the lasso away from the boy as punishment.
Then seeing how matters went, and remembering how boys
were in Portsdown, Osberne, quite forgetting that they did not
understand his speech, said, " Forgive the lad. It was done in
play and I know how boys are, for it is not so long since I did
tricks upon strangers." And though the words meant nothing,
yet the meaning was understood, so the man returned the lasso
to the boy and the boy flashed white teeth in a grin, then said
something to Osberne which he took to mean, " And for that
kindness I shall be at your service." So all went very well
indeed.

Then Ato began to talk, and Osberne knew, by one sign
and another, that he told the Indians what the men of the five
ships wanted, and very soon there grew much activity with
lads and young men getting ready their arrows, and their
lassos, and a weapon new to Osberne in the shape of three hide-
covered balls the size of an egg, fastened with hide strips
in such fashion that each strip was more than three feet long,
the three ends knotted together.

So the hunt began. And so also began a joyful day. Seaward they went, six hunters, and six lads running with guanacos in the rear, all of them making much merriment. Before
they had gone a mile, Osberne saw one of the tricks of the

weapon with the three balls. For they came upon a lake, not a large one, but reed-covered at its edges, and out flew a dozen or more gray geese with much honking and flapping. The boy who had thrown the lasso chanced to be close to Osberne who stood amazed seeing the swiftness with which the lad loosed his weapon. Taking the thongs at the joint and one of the

balls in his right hand he swung the two balls around his head in circles in such fashion that they stood apart and in a straight line, and next he loosed the other ball so that the weapon flew among the geese while the three balls formed a triangle, striking down the birds, four of them at a single shot. The weapon went circling and turning in the air, to fall on the other side of the lake.

"Well done! Well done!" called out Osberne, not remembering that they understood nothing of what he said. But all that day he shouted out sayings for very joy, much as if he had been at Portsdown, so that towards the end of the day the Indians caught up easy sayings and repeated them. "Well done!" they came to say. Or " good lad! " Or " there it is! " And Osberne, on his side, came to say " te-ya! " which meant " haste! " and " koo! " which meant " here," and " wee-ha-ko! " which meant, as he found, " go with care! "

With the three balls and thongs they caught two wild guanacos, casting the weapon in such fashion that it tangled the legs of the animals. An ostrich they also caught in the same way. Then they busied themselves cutting up the meat, and hanging the burden on the tame guanacos after it was well cleaned, and so, blithely, they went to the bay and to the seashore where Osberne hailed the ships and waited with his Indian companions until the boats came ashore.

But when the boats came near it angered Osberne to see bow-men in one of them, their arrows all ready, the more because at the sight of that his Indian companions also prepared their shafts. That took place in the boat where Espinosa sat as captain with the pilot Carvalho as steersman. The other boat, steered by Andrew, carried no weapons.

" Dog and coward! " shouted Osberne, in high anger, " you cannot come slaying these my friends. Lay down your arms, or, as I am a man, I shall send an arrow through your black heart, Espinosa."

" Said I not so? This fellow is a traitor," Osberne heard Espinosa say to Carvalho, and the words came clear because the boat was near the shore and the evening air very still. But Osberne took a bow from Ato and fitted an arrow to the string and then drew, but did not let fly. Thereupon his Indian companions prepared themselves.

"Put down your weapons," cried Espinosa to his men. "And tarry awhile so that the other boat goes first." Thus it came about that Andrew's boat passed the other boat and touched shore and the honest sailor stepped out and walked up to Osberne and took him by the hand. Then Osberne taught him the way of greeting in the Indian fashion, so Andrew went up the beach, his hands held high to show his friendship, and presently made friends with Ato and the rest by putting his right hand on their left shoulders and looking them in the eyes. But Osberne, full of anger against Espinosa would not let the fellow do more than stand knee-deep in the water while the boats were being loaded, and, to insure safety, he put the boy who had thrown the lasso as guard to watch him, to the Indian boy's great content. Not once did the lad release his bow string but kept it tight stretched, with the arrow notched, so that presently Espinosa went on his knees in the water for very fear and weariness.

"Now this is a wonder that these savages should speak English," said Hans, hearing the Indians say "there it is!" And "good lad!" and "well done!" as they carried the meat to the boats. And when two, bearing the geese, stopped to laugh at the sight of Espinosa on his knees in the water, and when Osberne said to them "ta-ya!" at which they made more speed, then not only Hans but all the sailors were amazed.

"Speak, speak!" they said to Osberne, thinking that he knew the Indian tongue and marveling to hear it. And Osberne, grinning, used the little that he knew, telling a couple who carried part of the guanaco to go with care, saying, "wee-ha-ko!" at which they replied "good lad!" and "well done!"

though they knew what it meant no more than a silly parrot's chatter.

When the boats were loaded, to further defy Espinosa as well as to insure all being well, Osberne said, " I shall not leave the shore until your boat has gone and is halfway to the ship. So let your men not loiter, for the day is near done."

Espinosa's face went red as fire with anger.

" Shall we seize the fellow and have done with this? " asked Carvalho.

" Not now," answered Espinosa, and sat frowning, scratching his chin. " But the jackanapes shall suffer for this in good time. I doubt not but this is all a trap and that there are other savages hidden hereabouts. Pull for the ship."

So the men pulled while Andrew's boat waited until Osberne had said his farewells to his Indian companions. When the boat had gone a few yards, Ato and the rest of the band threw up their arms and gave a cry —

" Ma-ee-ya! Ma-ee-ya, Ota-bben! "

" It is good that all has fallen out thus," said Andrew. " Once I feared that there would be blood spilt."

" It might have been," answered Osberne, " but Master Espinosa would have been the target."

But that night on the ships there were joyful men with their bellies full of fresh and well cooked meat. Magellan too was happy with good cheer and stood a long while on the deck listening to the loud laughter, and to the snatches of song, and hearing now and then, some one calling from the shore, " Ma-ee-ya, Ota-bben! "

When Espinosa came presently with a tale of how he feared that Osberne would stir up the Indians against the ships, Magellan plucked his beard and looked at him for a long time without saying anything. Then, " Man, are you mad? " he asked. " Here for the first time things go well, and we have good will among the men, and a promise of good food, and safety on shore, then you come like a fool to stir up trouble. I would that all my company stood as honest as this lad Osberne. For my part I am ready to take up the cry, ' Ma-ee-ya, Ota-bben! ' "

" A stirrer-up of trouble," said Espinosa.

" Thou liest in thy throat," said Magellan angrily. " I think the men do well to call thee fox-face."

CHAPTER VI

How Osberne Became a Captain

MANY A hunting trip had Osberne with his friends. Sometimes Andrew and Hans went with him, sometimes a picked companion from some other ship, but whoever went must needs be a good hunter. So the fleet was well supplied with game and venison and fish, besides flesh new to them. Also from the Indians Osberne learned to brew a drink made of herbs, sucking the pleasant tasting liquid through a straw, and the sailors learned to brew and drink it, so that the scurvy under which some had suffered went clean away and every man became strong and healthy. But with April come, some of the Indians went to the far mountains and only a few remained, Ato among them.

Also in April it began to be talked among the men that the *Santiago,* being ready for sea, would take a cruise to explore the Patagonian coast and find the strait, Serrao being the captain. Great was the delight of Osberne and Andrew when they found their names among those to go on the *Santiago,* and greater their delight when they learned that Espinosa would stay with Magellan in San Julian Bay. But when Osberne told Ato what was afoot the Indian said that it was well enough, for he and his party could not stay longer about the bay because of the scarcity of game, but would themselves go south for a time. "And," said he, "we shall meet somewhere, as men always do in this land, for friends stay not apart." All those months had made for understanding so that Osberne knew much of the Indian speech, and Ato some English.

Then came the day of sailing, when the *Santiago* went out of the bay with flags flying, and the men cheering, and bombards thundering in salute, and farewells shouted from the other ships. When they were out in the open again, on a sunlit and sparkling sea, not a man there but felt his heart leap with joy to see the dancing spray, and to taste the brine on his lips, and to feel the heaving deck under his feet. It was good to see the white gulls, and the porpoises that played about the bows, and the sails swelling before the freshening wind. Merrily danced the little ship to a joyous music of straining ropes, and creaking blocks, and the splash of water against the black sides.

And down in the ship's hold were good salted fish and meat, and sweet water, with everywhere above and below clean as man could wish all to be. So the *Santiago* sailed south, a ship full of joy and courage and peace, its men strong and whole-some and busy, a living purpose in them. It was good to hear the snatches of songs that the men sang, and the loud voice of the ship's master, and the ringing of the ship's bell. To Os-berne, standing at the tiller and feeling the press of the ship, the troubles he had known were like ripples on a pool, the sting of them passed and near forgotten. Not a man sailed on that ship but was brave and glad-hearted, a most glorious company.

Presently they came to a river, and because they entered it when the cross of stars set in that sky came out, they named it the Santa Cruz, and there they anchored. Nor had any of them seen a place in which were so many fish most delicate to eat. Also there were animals called sea-wolves, but which one who had sailed in far northern seas said were seals.

"Saw ever man so fine a place for fish?" asked Serrao the Captain, and Osberne, who heard, whispered to Andrew, "Yes, I did. For here I came with Ato more than once." It is no more than sixty miles from the bay, though to be sure it seems more, sailing as we did round a great cape."

Six days they stayed there, fishing and salting the fish for the fleet, then loading it into the ship. Serrao, thinking that it would be well to know the river, ordered the men to get out a boat, which they did, and six stout rowers went in it. The river ran swift and they made little way, except at flood-tide, so, coming to the place where the tide water ended, they turned back.

Then they sailed again, but into an unkind sea. There came a day with light winds in the morning, not blowing from one point, but now from this and now from that, so the captain held close to land looking for a harbor or a sheltered place in the lee of some point, but the rock-bound coast offered no haven, and the waves broke white at the foot of the cliffs, and great black rocks showed. So they stood out to sea again. At noon the wind dropped and the sails hung loose, and the sun turned to a sickly yellow, but all the while the sea heaved in great sullen waves, not green or blue, but brown. And the waves grew greater as the day wore, so that the ship pitched and foundered, though they did not break over the deck, but lifted the craft. When the wind came it leaped at them so fiercely that two of the sails split to ribbons, and the world seemed full of strange shriekings and screamings as though raging giants flew through the air. So the ship, lacking sails, lay helpless, sadly buffeted by wrathful waves that swept the deck and tore the boats away, while the men wrestled and struggled to keep their hold. One man, the negro servant of Serrao, was picked up as he tried to lash himself against the mast; picked up and cast again on the deck where he lay washed this way and that in raging and foaming water, trying to catch at some hold but always torn away as though his hands had no more strength than the hands of a child. Once Andrew caught at him and the negro found his feet, but a roaring, white-topped wave came and bore him across the deck and overboard, so he was lost.

Near nightfall they could see the shore gaunt and grim, but because of the set of the current and the direction of the wind the ship did not drift shoreward, so in spite of their trouble they had hopes that the storm might be weathered. But a mighty sea came, a towering black wall rimmed with white that blotted out the stars and fell thundering on the ship, breaking off one of the masts and splitting the deck. Another sea lifted the craft and carried it landward, then flung it on to the rocks at the base of a tall cliff. For weary hours other waves lifted and let the ship fall so that the timbers cracked and gaped, and sea water ran in and out of the ship, and the ribs of the vessel were ground and broken. One by one the men dropped into the sea and were lost to sight, swept landward.

Nor did Osberne ever know how he was torn away from his hold. Once he found himself in the sea, battling strongly, hearing no noise at all because the world of waters was all noise, and seeing sometimes a flash of lightning that split the firmament. Then all went black. But again he heard the screaming storm and found his mind clear, though he was like one who had come out of depths of inky darkness to light. He did not think of his death but, as in a flash, of his companions and of the sport and play they had known. Then he seemed to be tired and about to go to sleep, whereupon he said to himself, " Now, Osberne of Portsdown, play the man! " Again a black, chill night opened to receive him but he woke again to struggle and swim on his back, with his feet shoreward, so that he would be flung on his face by the wave, for the sea seemed somewhat quieter because of a sheltering point, as he afterwards found. Next he felt a sharp pain in his knee, and could dimly see the cliff, then he felt the sliding sand under his hands that clutched. But for a while his scrambling availed him little because the backwater dragged him. He overcame that presently and lay on the stones above the water, wondering in a dull way at the beating of his heart which seemed as if it would burst his side.

When he woke again it was in the small hours of morning and the wind still blew fiercely. He felt heartened to know that he was not dead. So he turned over to lie on his back, but his mind was confused because it seemed to him that the world had changed somehow, and the sea and land were not where he thought them to be, but turned round another way. When he tried to stand up, then, "Day of miracles!" he said, "I am alive but every bone in my body must be broken." For he ached from top to toe, and his joints were stiff, and his head throbbed, and every inch of him was as sore as if it had been belabored with a stick. And his mind was nearly as benumbed as his body, but he fell to rubbing himself until the blood flowed freely again through his limbs, and then he made shift to stand up, though at first he reeled like a drunken man.

A good way out to sea lay the ship, her rigging broken and her deck stripped off. And, it being low tide, though rising, the rocks showed all tangled with seaweed, and here and there a plank or a piece of wreckage. The main-mast and a spar or two lay near him and seeing them he thanked his patron saint that some of it had not knocked him on the head. Also here and there along the sand lay men, though if they were dead or alive he could not know. So he went to this one and to that, shaking and waking them. Some were very wroth, thinking themselves on the ship and called too early. Others seemed moon-struck and stupid. Others called for water. But Serrao, the Captain, sat in a niche like a little cave at the foot of a cliff, a man very much ashamed because of the loss of his ship, and taking the blame of it all to himself. Andrew he did not find for a long time, and when he met him it was a good distance away and on the other side of a high cape, the sailor not stretched out as if dead, but walking in a stumbling way.

"Saints be with us!" called out his friend, "I thought every man dead but I. Here I woke on this side of the cape and saw the ship all broken, but no soul except the dead body of the negro. Well, ships will run ashore, and ships have run ashore before now, but with the most of our shipmates alive it matters very little."

"You call it only running ashore?" said Osberne, amazed. "It seemed to me the greatest shipwreck that ever could be. Was ever storm so great? Saw you before anything like it? I thought the very heavens would split."

"Not once but five times have I been cast away," said Andrew. "As for the greatness of the storm, belike it came as a fearful thing to you who have seen little more than fair weather. But this is no great tale to tell, lad, though the man Pigafetta who writes and writes, and much of the writing lies because he puts down hearsay, he will have much to say about it. But of such things a sailor is silent."

After that Osberne said no more about the storm, nor, as he noticed, did the older seamen talk much about it. But they had very much to say about the lack of food, and very much to say about the dangers from wild animals and savages on shore. As landsmen fear a sea voyage and look for death from drowning on the fairest of sailing days, so were the seamen fearful of land terrors. Nothing that they could eat had come ashore from the wreck, therefore in that barren place they saw naught but starvation facing them. When a cold rain came up that morning, they sat huddled under the cliff, grumbling and asking one another what could be done. And thus they were when Osberne and Andrew found them. But Serrao stood apart, a man so sorrowful because of the loss of his ship that every man pitied him.

"Shipmates, what shall we do?" asked Andrew, and they looked at him and he looked at them, every man there wondering to see how soon his fellow man had turned into a scarecrow. Hardly one but stood in rags with nothing to cover his nakedness save shirt and breeches.

For answer they began to grumble.

" Here is death of starvation," said one.

" We shall be food for cannibals," said another.

" May God have mercy on us," said a third.

Another cursed very low. Another said that if they had food and strength they might fashion some sort of raft and somehow sail back to the bay. Another clasped his hands, as if in prayer, and spoke of fishhooks, saying that if he had one he would feed every man there, given time.

" Andrew," said Osberne, " if you will get flint and steel and make a fire, I may catch fish enough without hooks, by an Indian trick," but he said it in a low voice, partly because he feared to boast and partly because he was not sure that he had the skill to win.

So Andrew set to work to find dry moss, and Osberne took the page whose name was Juan and went a little way along the sea-beach until he came upon some scraps of food that had been washed ashore. After gathering the scraps he carried them to a place where an inlet ran up into the land, and there he scattered the food. Next, across the mouth of the inlet he, with the page helping, built a low wall of stones. At another bay-like place they did the same, also at a third and a fourth and a fifth place, until they had used all the food scraps.

" If all goes well as I hope," said Osberne, " and as it did when Ato did the same thing and taught me, then with the tide there will come fish. And as the tide lowers again and the water runs out, we shall walk across and across, close to and on the seaside of the little walls thus keeping the fish in, should there be any. But if the plan fails, then we shall say nothing."

While the tide rose to its full they went to suitable dank places and found mushrooms, which they gathered. Also they picked mussels from the rocks until the water covered them so that they could gather no more. And by the side of a narrow stream they found wild celery. A long time all that took, but they found it better to be busy than idle. At last, at the turn of the tide, they went back to the walls and in three of the pools were fish leaping, many dozens of them. Some escaped, swimming through the spaces between the stones, or sometimes leaping over the walls, but there were enough left behind, gasping and flapping, when the tide had gone. Those they threw out on the shore, then called the men to take what they wanted. Then there came a great to-do of cooking fish on spits, and of opening mussels by laying them on hot stones, and of eating mushrooms and looking for more of them. Those who had been downcast grew lighter and grumbled the heavier, and those who had grumbled and growled began to plan, for full bellies change the world, as the saying runs.

For four days they worked at low tide, taking ashore such timbers as they could carry, also finding stores from the ship such as barrels of salted meat, and salted fish, and pots for cooking. But the weapons they found were utterly spoiled and unfit for use, except the knives and an ax. So Osberne remembered the Indian weapon with the three balls and thongs of hide which he called boledores, and after some trouble fashioned one, but so roughly that it was of no use. As soon as Andrew understood the nature of the weapon he went to work, and, being a skillful man with his hands, made a good one. Thereupon Osberne went with it up the beach and on top of the cliff and practiced as he had seen the Indians do, throwing at a stick he had set up. For a while he hurt himself sadly, tangling the thongs and getting them about his own legs, or whirling unhandily and cracking his own head with the balls, but at last came to making a fair cast. So, being ready to try his skill, he went with the page, who was much afraid of cannibals leaping upon him for a time, and then walked a half league into the country, Osberne being minded to try another trick that he had learned from the Indians. Fortune was with them and near noon they saw four of the yellow and white animals called the guanaco, but so far away that the strongest bowman with the best of bows could not have sent a shaft within fifty yards of the nearest of the creatures.

"Never shall we eat that meat," said the page.

"Curiosity brought the fox to the trap," said Osberne. "Do you go to that hillock and lie on your back, then kick your legs in the air."

"Am I a fool to do so, or are you mad?" answered Juan.

"Neither," said Osberne. "Thus I have seen an Indian do, and it worked well. I will hide near by, then try a cast at the right time, but it may be that my skill shall fail. Yet I tell you for a truth this animal can be killed because of its curiosity."

"I do not believe, but shall make the trial," said Juan, and went to the hillock, then laid himself down as Osberne had told him to do, and began kicking his heels in the air. Osberne hid behind a dwarf thorn bush.

At first the guanaco went on grazing. Then the greatest one stood with head upraised, a creature proud and noble to see. Slowly it drew near, not walking in a straight line to the kicking page, but making circles, keeping first one eye and then the other on the kicking legs. Nearer it came, full of caution, but stopped and ran off a little way, then stood again, watchful and full of grace, turning its head to see first with one eye, then with the other, as a chicken does.

" It wonders," thought Osberne, " because on all this plain there is no tree or bush, only these legs kicking. It must look at the strange thing just as a man on a ship steers out of his way to see a boat when that boat and no other is in sight."

A pity came over Osberne that he must kill the creature, for it was soon close by. Eight feet above ground was its head, four feet its shoulders, and when it walked it stepped daintily. From a distance the three other guanacos watched it, and, as Osberne knew, having learned from Ato, did the guanaco once give its shrill cry, then all of the animals would fly like the wind.

" Never did I feel so like a traitor," Osberne told himself. " This is the guard and sentinel with his heart on the safety of his fellows, yet I must slay it. My heart tells me that it is as if I stained mine honor. But then a starved belly has no ears, and hunger is a sharp, fierce dog."

So he prepared his boledores as he lay, swinging them in little circles and letting out the thongs. But as soon as the air began to whistle because of the swinging, the guanaco lifted its ears, gave a shrill cry and darted off. Then Osberne leaped to his feet and true to the mark flew the boledores, tangling about the forelegs of the animal and bringing it down. It half rose to its feet, but when Osberne saw its great dark eyes he could not bring himself to do more.

The page, Juan, came running, saying, " Now to make an end of it and cut up the meat," but Osberne shook his head.

" It is a foolish weakness that has come upon me, Juan," said Osberne. " Take you the knife, and I shall send Andrew and one or two others."

"Not so," said Juan. "Not for anything would I be left alone in this lonely place. There might come savages and cannibals. There might come strange beasts. Wait then until I have killed the animal so that it may not suffer, and we shall go together."

But Osberne's strange weakness passed after Juan had killed the guanaco, and together they skinned it and cut up the meat. Osberne took the hide, for he had a mind to make for himself a cloak such as the Indians wore. And that he presently did with Andrew's help. As for the meat, there was enough for ten men to carry back to the stream; and they cooked and ate it, and afterwards dried some of it in the wind and the sun, and so starvation grinned no more for a time.

It was hard work gathering the timbers and carrying them up above the high-water mark, and more than a week passed in the doing of it. Then Captain Serrao told the men what had best be done.

"If we wait here," he said, "until another of the fleet's ships comes to look for us, it may well be that we shall be passed without being seen. The ship may stand off. There may be a storm. Or seeing us from a distance they may take us for savages."

"We are all for making our way back," said one.

"Then we should walk into the land, going straight as may be, not following the sea with its windings and capes and bays," said Osberne.

"None of that for us," said another. "We are seamen and a cock is brave on his own dunghill. Among the savages we would be lost."

"And there are wild animals," said another.

"And what of the river Santa Cruz?" asked another.

"We must carry planks with us and make a raft," said Serrao.

"A heavy load for weary miles," said a sailor.

"There is food too to be carried," said another.

"I am for keeping by the sea, walking and watching," said Juan.

"But that way you will walk ten times the distance," said Osberne. "Going straight, by the land, we may get to the bay where the fleet is in a week."

"And maybe perish of thirst in the desert," grumbled another.

"We shall doubtless find holes of water," said Osberne. "The Indians do not perish of thirst. Besides, these wild animals drink."

"As well look for wings on a wolf as for water and food in a desert such as this," said the grumbler. "I am all for keeping to the seashore."

"And I."

"You speak for all."

"So say we."

"Leave well enough alone. We know the sea but do not know the land."

"Then," said Serrao, "I am minded to call for men to go over the land, in a straight line, while we keep to the sea-coast without burdens. If those who go overland, as Osberne says, make such short work of it, well and good. They can return with men from the fleet and find us. Does any one offer?"

But none stood forth.

"Osberne, will you go?" said Serrao.

"If you send me, gladly," said Osberne.

"And I offer," said Andrew.

" And I," said Juan

" Not so," said Serrao. " There are these burdens to bear and every shoulder will be needed. One is enough to go. Or at the most two."

" But why carry so much ? " asked Osberne. " Why not leave the timber and build no raft ? "

" How should we cross the Santa Cruz river ? " asked a man.

" Doubtless there is a ford up the river," said Osberne. " I will have to seek one. And the Indians who certainly cross the river must cross without rafts."

" It would be a search full of peril, looking for a ford," said another.

" Yet there must be one," said Osberne. " But if not, then where the river narrows I shall swim."

" That is bravely said," said Serrao. " But then you have friended with the savages."

Osberne laughed, then said, " As our shipmate said, ' A cock is brave on his own dunghill.' I am much at home on the land. I was faint-hearted on the ship in the storm."

" Osberne," said Serrao, " it may be that you face a danger to help us. It may be that you have the easiest path. Who shall say? There may be trials and hardships. But let me say this. Do not fear if things go not well, to come back to us with the task undone. We shall know that you faced what you had to face. It is a man's work. Do your best. You have done well before this. May you do well in this."

Hearing that, Osberne's heart glowed within him and he felt strong. He could find nothing to say, but stood there, looking at the ground.

" I shall give you my sword," said Serrao, and began to undo his belt.

" Captain, I thank you," answered Osberne. " But it is no country for swords. It were better to go as the Indians go. Seeing me armed as they are, and with nothing more, they will make no trouble. Arms are a trouble to one without the will to kill, and I have no will to kill."

So they all stood looking at one another saying nothing for a little while, then Osberne bade them farewell and went up the cliff and into the land. Nor would any have known him for what he was, for he wore about his neck a cloak made of the guanaco, and his hair was long like that of an Indian, and to keep it out of his eyes he had bound a fillet of hide about his forehead. On his legs were a kind of shoes made out of the guanaco hide bound round with thongs, a foot-wear soft and serviceable. His breeches had been torn until what was left looked like the loin cloth such as Ato had. Round his waist he carried the boledores, his only weapon. For the rest he was a lad golden-skinned, tall, straight, his eyes bright and shining. So, as he stood on the edge of the cliff, slim against the sky, the men laughed and said to one another that if they had not known him for their shipmate they would have fled, or would have hidden, believing him to be an Indian. And Osberne, looking down at the sailors trudging along the beach carrying boards, and meats, and pots, and many other things, laughed because they looked like ants.

" A sad piece of business to send a lad on so perilous a journey," said one man, who was carrying the end of a plank of no light weight, to his fellow.

" He seemed to go with a light heart," said the other, " but to a young heart everything is sport."

" And a good heart breaks a bad fortune," said a man who carried a piece of flesh.

" But then consider the lonesomeness," said a third, shifting a great water jar to his other shoulder. " With us, company in misery makes misery light."

" And company makes short miles," put in another man who was all hung about with copper pots that clattered as he walked.

" The weight of loneliness is greater than the weight of this basket of fish," added Juan, the page.

So many of the men were very sorry for Osberne.

But he went on into the country full of joyousness, light of heart and light of foot. He was ravished with joy at the cloud-flecked sky, and the wide horizon, and the wind that blew through his hair. And when he came to a hill and looked out to sea and beheld the running waves that broke white, and then saw inland the other sea of tall pampas grass, he wanted to shout aloud. For very happiness he ran, sometimes for a mile and more. Then he fell to casting his boledores, whirling and letting them go and finding delight in running swiftly to try if he could catch them as they fell, as he had seen an Indian boy do, but which he could not do at all. And towards noon there came out of the sky, to follow him, great birds as large as an eagle, crested and black, with fierce beaks, a sort he had seen following the Indians when they hunted, to steal the meat. His heart rose high at the sight of swans, and flamingos, and a small scarlet-breasted bird the like of which he had not seen before. He saw herons and storks and owls that lived in holes in the ground; a bird that darted down on a snake and slew it; a gray ostrich that ran across his path and vanished in a light mist; a falcon like those he had seen in Portsdown and which lords and ladies hunted with; hawks and doves and ducks; field-mice and fawns and great toads and frogs; all these he saw and called good luck on them. And at night he lay down for the dark hours and for a while listened to a bird that sang like a flute, which seemed to him most enchanting music. But he was tired with the tiredness that is a pleasure, so soon fell asleep.

He rose with the sun and after eating some of the food he had brought with him went on his way, but he had gone a scant half hour when he saw a guanaco, a small one, yet full grown, and it amazed him that instead of running away it came towards him. So he stood and held out his hand and the creature halted, looking at him with head upraised. Nor did it move when he drew nearer. Then he knew it to be one of the tame animals that the Indians used, so Osberne thought that a camp might be near, though he soon found that a false thought.

" Now," said Osberne to the animal, " you live in a happy land, knowing no fear. Had you been a horse, and in my country, then you would have run from a man, lest he give you a beating. So let us try a journey together."

Thereupon he turned the guanaco in the way he would go, and, laying a hand on its shoulder made the clicking noise with his tongue that Ato had taught him. So the guanaco sped onward, Osberne holding a hand to its shoulder, and in that fashion many miles slipped under man and beast. But near evening they came to a place of soft grass where the animal stopped and put down its head to eat, so Osberne left it, after saying a farewell, and went on his way alone.

Near twilight time he came to a hill on the side of which stood much long grass, and there he stopped to rest for the time of dark. While he ate he heard a noise in the grass and, on looking up, his heart stood still, for there lay a great tawny beast like a lion, its eyes gleaming green and sometimes ruby, the tail of it waving gently.

Osberne put his hand behind him to grasp his boledores,

thinking to strike the lion on the head and sell his life at a good price, then, of a sudden, it came to his mind that Ato had said that the pampas lion was the friend of man, craving no man's blood, seeking no man's life. Yet Osberne gave a sigh and his hand trembled somewhat. But he let the boledores lie, then got to his knees, and next to his feet, then felt his face go red because of the fear that had been in him.

"Now," said Osberne, trying to cheer himself with his own voice, "let us be friends."

So he put out his hand and rubbed the pampas lion behind the ears as he had rubbed many a cat, nor did the animal show teeth or claws. Soon he patted it and slapped it lightly, and he laughed when the creature rose to its feet and made a low noise in its throat, a noise of pleasure, and after that rubbed against his legs and wound back and forth.

"The thing to wonder at, friend," said Osberne, "is how this is to end. I have no mind to keep you as a sleeping companion, nor have I mind to drive you from your bed."

Then he bethought him of his meat, so he gave that to the lion, which ended the matter, for the great beast walked away.

"The full belly hates a long sermon, as they say," said Osberne. "So farewell. But it would seem that I have been a friend and a fool too, for now must I go hungry."

That hunger was short lived, for on the next day Osberne came to the Santa Cruz river as he knew he would, by a low hill which he saw for many miles. Four hundred yards of milky-blue water running swiftly lay between him and the other bank, and when Osberne looked across he thought of his empty stomach. But he told himself that a good beginning was half the work, so took to the water. Yet he had not thought of the swiftness of the current; and in the middle, where it ran deep, the water carried him down so quickly that the bank seemed to be rushing away. More than eight miles he was borne, nor did he try to fight the tide but let himself go with it, edging little by little, so at last stepped on the other shore a tired and hungry lad.

So there was, as he judged, fifty miles to go before he reached the bay where the fleet lay, but it would be fifty miles without food, except berries and such herbs as he knew, for he had no way of making fire, and much wished that he had learned the art by rubbing sticks on wood, as he had seen Ato do. Nor did the country wear a pleasant face, for the green of it had gone and everywhere were low thorn bushes and tufts of brown, sere grass. So Osberne sat awhile by the river after he drank his fill, wondering much how things would fall out in the crossing of that plain, for it was clear that the water holes had dried up.

"It will be feeble going," he told himself, "but a man must struggle on. He who gives up turns his shield the wrong way."

So he made tighter his girdle and set off, whistling to forget his hunger, but made a poor job of that. And when he had gone some twenty miles, a strange thing befell him, which was this. Having gained the top of a long and low hill what should he see but the smoke of a fire, and, stopping to look, made out the figures of men which he knew were not Indians but shipmates. So he guessed, and rightly, that a party had been sent out from the fleet to look at the land and report. At once new life came to him with the thought of good food, and good talk, and a bed. Whereupon he started to run, and in a few steps more had lost sight of the fire because of the lay of the land, which was somewhat like the waves of the sea in that place. But when he reached the top of the next rise he saw the fire and the men again, so waved his cloak to gain their notice, though to no effect. On he went again, making great haste, sometimes shouting, though that he told himself was the work of a fool. So, on the crest of the fourth rise he found himself almost upon his shipmates, less than an arrow's flight indeed.

He gave a great shout, seeing that the six of them were busy about their fire, making a meal. Then one of the men looked up and pointed. Also three or four seized their bows and fitted arrows, whereupon Osberne remembered how he looked like an Indian. So he took off his cloak and waved it, crying out, "Hold your hands, shipmates!" but they did not hear, or hearing did not understand. Thereupon he threw up his hands to show that he had no weapon, but the fools were full of panic and three of them let fly arrows, but all very wide of the mark except one. And the arrow of that one found Osberne's body in the fleshy part of the left shoulder, passing through and sticking out a hand's breadth behind.

"Fools, and cowards, and swinish hearts!" shouted Osberne, shaking his fist. But the men neither heard nor saw, for they were in full flight away from their camp and into the forty miles between them and the bay. At first Osberne was so filled with rage that he heeded not the pain, but when his anger passed he turned sick, seeing the blood that laced his skin. And the pain that shot through his hurt arm, when he lifted it, stung like a hive of bees, but he had to raise it to grasp the shaft near the head and break it with his right hand. Then he drew out the arrow in two parts and the blood gushed forth.

Happily he found water in plenty in the camp, and washed his wound. Then he went to work most heartily on the food, so that he well-nigh finished the stew that had been made for six men. But his shoulder burned with a shooting pain as if a red-hot iron had been thrust through the flesh, and he was a happy lad when he found a plant with a broad leaf, of which the Indians had told him, which when soaked in water and laid on the wound eased the pain. For all that he slept well, which amazed him in the morning, for he had feared a night of tossing about in pain. "Of a truth," he said to himself when he had risen and was preparing a good meal of cold boiled goose, "of a truth a man who remembers not that he slept ill, must have slept well." Yet his hurt arm was stiff and swollen and flaming sore.

"Now," said he, talking to himself, "it is time to call for a cool head. These men with no thought but to shoot and to slay found no spring of water but carried what is here. Ato and the boy Kenu once told me to give ear to the bird-voices if I would find water."

So he stood stock-still using his ears, counting the sounds, some of them loud and near, others faint and far off. And he remembered how the Indians had taught him that birds that fly above ground make no great noise because they can see far; but those that live in bushes and in reeds and on the ground make much noise calling one to another because they cannot see their mates and companions. Soon, from among many other sounds, he caught the sorrowful scream of a gray spotted bird like a thrush that lived in the reeds, but far away. Then, as if another bird had joined in to tell them it was truth, he caught the sweet song of a great bird like a swan that lives in marshes but flies high, singing the while, then drops again to the water. Having marked from whence the sound came he went that way, over a hill and across a flat land somewhat stony, and so came to a reed-edged lake well-sheltered from winds by hills around. So he thrust himself through the reeds and lay down in the cool water, and bathed and washed the wound until the fire went out of it.

It seemed well, too, that he went out of his course somewhat, because when he started again he found a pleasant way between hills that ran down to the sea, and came to a clear, bright stream. And when the sun came up, for he walked by the stream all night, there in a wedge of light between green hills lay the sea, and the four ships. But at sight of them a sorrow fell on him because in the ships were men who brought pain and trouble into a land of peace. The world without them lay fair and clean, but they came with fire and sword to spoil. They came like jangling noise shattering sweet music. They came, not to see and to enjoy, but to lay waste and to slay, to awaken anger and unrest. They came in their selfishness. They came to turn beauty into dust and ashes. They came to turn order into disorder. So it was with a heavy heart that Osberne went down to the sea.

But again he forgot that he looked like an Indian, so when he came near to where some of the fleet worked, patching up a boat with pitch on the beach, two of the sailors caught up pikes and shouted to others to arm themselves.

"The savages are upon us!" he heard a man cry.

"To the ship!" called another, and began to push off the boat. Osberne stood still, his hands thrown apart, somewhat troubled until he saw the red beard of Hans. Then he called out to his friend. "Hans! It is Osberne and no stranger. Do you know me?"

"By all the saints!" cried the sailor, and threw down his ladle of pitch and ran to Osberne. Then he rattled out questions waiting for no answer. "How art thou? What hath gone wrong? Where is the ship? What of Andrew and Juan and Serrao? How came ye wounded? How came ye alone? Saw ye six sailors?"

"As to the six sailors, they did all the wounding that was done," answered Osberne. "Six such fools sent into such a land as this are half a dozen too many."

So they talked as they rowed to the *Trinidad,* and there Espinosa met the boat, and seeing Osberne hailed him.

"The admiral," he said, "must know what of the *Santiago.*"

"It is wrecked beyond hope," answered Osberne, "but I myself shall tell the tale to the captain-general."

"It will be well first to tell it to me," answered Espinosa. "The captain-general is on board the *San Antonio* and busy with affairs. I shall see to it that he gets the news when he is in the right mood. There are worries from which he must be shielded."

"Tell whatsoever tale you choose to tell," said Osberne. "But it will be no tale of mine turned around and made to suit yourself."

Espinosa stood speechless for a moment, looking down at Osberne who stood in the boat with a foot on the thwart, but, nothing shamed, the lad stood the straighter. "There have been tongues that cut their own throats," said Espinosa, and frowned darkly.

"Let us go to the captain-general," said Osberne, speaking to the men in the boat.

"I gave no order," said Espinosa.

"Hearken, Espinosa," said Osberne. "I come from Serrao, I am his messenger. Alone I come. I have a message and news, and a straight tale may make all well. A crooked tale would make more crookedness, and you can tell no other than a tale not straight. If you would give orders, then let your order be one that sends me to the captain-general without delay."

"It is a matter of right," said Espinosa, swallowing down what he did not like as best he could. "I shall take you to the captain-general." With that he stepped into the boat and told the men to row to the *San Antonio,* which they did.

And as soon as Magellan saw the boat, and Osberne in it, "Here is my truth-teller," he said, though not cheerfully, for as a usual thing he was no cheerful man. So Osberne climbed aboard, very brisk in spite of being weary, and saluted Magellan.

"You are travel worn," said Magellan. "I should have taken you to be an Indian. Or have you deserted again to join them?"

"Captain-general," said Osberne, "a bagpipe makes noise only when its belly is full. May I ask a favor?"

"What is it?"

"Let me eat and talk as I eat. I am faint with hunger and thirst. Then let the barber dress my wound. Thus I shall be ready to start again, for there is no time to lose."

"Now if there is another man in the fleet who would talk in that fashion, I would not know where to look for him," said Magellan. "If that was the fashion in which you talked to your English lord, small wonder that things went well."

So it came about that Magellan and Osberne again sat together at one end of the deck, and the lad told his tale while he ate, and answered many questions while the barber dressed his wound, which he did very skillfully.

"There is a favor I would ask, Captain-general," said Osberne at the end.

" You would not ask one I could not grant if you are the
lad I take you to be," said Magellan, somewhat surlily as was
his way. " What is it? "

" This. That you let not Espinosa lay hands on any of what
I do, because only he who knows can guide. Give me ten
men and let me lead them. I shall thus find Serrao and his
men and bring them back. But without knowledge there
can be no success."

" You hate our Espinosa," said Magellan.

" I hate not the man, but the failure that he is," answered
Osberne. " And I hate him because of the disorder he brings
everywhere."

They sat silent for a while, then Osberne said, " Give me
leave to take ten men, and if not ten then six, and if not six
then two, and I will bring back Serrao and his men."

" But why so many men? " asked Magellan.

Quick as a flash came the answer, " Because there may be
some sick. Because we must carry food."

" And because there may be battle," put in Magellan.

" Not that," said Osberne. " We will take no arms. This is
a land of peace, not war."

" And when would you set off? "

" Within the hour."

" But you need rest."

" We shall sleep to-night and I can go until then, waking
refreshed with the sun. Under the sky a man does not tire
in the weary way he tires when cooped up."

" Then," said Magellan, " it shall be so. You shall be Captain Osberne until your return. I will say no word. I will not
hinder or help. And if on your return you swear loyalty to
me and to my side, then there may be other things to come."

"I would there were no fighting sides, only a body and a proper head," said Osberne.

"But a thing with two heads cannot fare well," answered Magellan. "Therefore one head must be destroyed. Therefore there are fighting sides."

"And the body dies while the heads fight," said Osberne.

"Too bold, my lad. Too bold," said Magellan, but without anger. Then he added, "But it is pardoned in Captain Osberne."

When the news of Osberne's captaincy got about the fleet, and it flew somehow, and when the ten men had been chosen and had taken their places in the boat, Espinosa went to Magellan full of complaint. It was folly, he said, for the men to go unarmed, because even while the talk with Osberne had been going on the party sent to see the land had returned with tales of Indian warfare. They had been attacked by a band of fierce savages and although they fought bravely had been forced to flee, leaving their camp. There they were, said Espinosa, weak and famished, sore stricken because of many dangers. So it would be right and proper to send an armed force, and he would be glad enough to go.

"Captain Osberne!" called Magellan, looking down into the boat. "How many Indians saw ye?"

"None," answered Osberne.

"And why, think you, did the six men of the fleet flee so fast after sending an arrow through you?"

"Doubtless to carry the news that I was on the way," said Osberne trying to put on an air of humble modesty, though he grinned as he spoke. He added, "I was the one they took to be a party of savages."

Then Magellan turned to Espinosa. "You see, it is said

that fear has big eyes. Mark how true the saying. For one lad, near famished, is turned by fearful eyes to a band of fierce savages. But enough. Espinosa, let a bombard be fired as salute for Captain Osberne."

"I fear there are men of noble blood in the fleet who will not like this," said Espinosa.

"It is more noble to make yourself great than to be born so," answered Magellan shortly, then turned away.

So the bombard bellowed as the men bent to their oars, and thus Osberne started on his rescue. And all was well, for they went by the way of the lake that Osberne found, so that they lacked no water, then straight as the crow flies to Santa Cruz river. Two days' journey up the river they came to a good ford, with many tracks of guanacos, and ostrich, and Indians, so there they crossed; then went on down until they came to the sea-beach. There they found Serrao and his men, all of them weary and worn, and without the burdens they had started with, for those they had thrown aside. They had not dared to leave the sea-coast fearing they would be slain by cannibals and eaten. Some, indeed, had been for going no further but waiting for help to come, but they had changed their minds when Serrao and Andrew and a few of the sturdy ones went on, making as if to leave them. But a good meal and a good sleep set the most of them to rights though they were too weary to make much haste over the plains, so that it was twenty-five days from the time they were wrecked until they set foot on the decks of the ships in San Julian Bay.

CHAPTER VII

How Osberne Lost his Captaincy

AT LAST came the time when the fleet was ready to
leave, but Osberne had little to do with its getting
ready for he had been found of greatest use in playing hunter, a something he did gladly because he loved the life
on the plains, more gladly because the Indians had returned,
Ato and the boy Kenu with them. Day after day the hunters
brought guanaco meat, and deer, and armadillo, and wild
geese and ducks, good fat meat all of it which the sailors salted
and laid away. Then there were eggs of geese and of gulls,

and of the ostrich and a great duck that lives by the sea in the cliffs. Sometimes Osberne would be with the Indians for days together, seeing the ships only when they brought the meat down to the beach. But the word had gone forth that he must return to the ship within two days, because they had meat enough, which message was brought to him by the boy Kenu. So Osberne's heart was heavy at having to say a farewell to his brave companions; but his duty bound him to the ship.

Osberne stood in the Indian camp looking at his companions where many had gathered together, all of whom he knew and loved, for it had been agreed that on the Friday there would be a farewell feast, then, on the Saturday, Osberne must rejoin the fleet. From the hilltop on which he stood he could see the bay and the little waves that broke about the ships, for it was a bright sunny day. So his heart was torn between the companions in the fleet and the companions of the pampas. And the Indians were dear to him. Brave men he knew them to be, brave and kindly. That day they had given over to play, running races, throwing lances, shooting with the bow, wrestling, casting the boledores and throwing the lasso. And after the sport, the women served a feast and sang songs. Then the chief, a tall man and noble, stood a little apart and made a sign. So there came girls who brought gold-dust in baskets, and bright red stones, and pieces of gold, all of which the children were used to play with, but which the men, for the sake of the beauty of the thing, sometimes made into arm rings.

" I know not why the men on the ships set such great store by this yellow dust and these stones," said the chief. " Perhaps it is for the glitter of them. But to be pleased with glitter seems to me, your chief Amelkima, a childish thing. Two days ago Kenu went to the ships with meat, and on his arm he bore a ring of this glitter. Now what did the man with the fox-face do but take it from the lad, not gently either. Kenu held his hand, and forbore to strike him. But your fox-face of the ships himself had glittering things, such as his knife handle. Had Kenu taken that, then fox-face would have fought. Ota-bben, our friend, may know why the men of the ships are like hungry wolves for this yellow stuff. Stand forth, Ota-bben and teach us."

The chief sat down and the people called out in a loud voice, "Ma-ee-ya, Amelkima, our beloved chief!" When Osberne stood up, they called again, "Ma-ee-ya, Ota-bben!" So Osberne raised his right hand in salute and spoke.

"This yellow stuff," he began, "our people call gold; and some there are who set it above everything in the world, even friendship, even life itself." Then he went on to tell of buying and of selling and of trading; how a man having killed meat would change it for gold, and how that one would find another who would give more gold for it. He told how ships were sent out to all parts of the world for gold, and how one ship robbed another. He told how a man would set bounds about a piece of land and stay there until some other offered gold for the plot of ground. He told how men in other lands robbed and slew one another for gold. And as he talked his mind ran on the wonder and folly of it all, for he had not seen that folly in its strength until then.

"And you say that a man having meat more than his needs, will not give it to one who starves, unless that starved one gives gold for it?" asked the chief, almost unbelieving.

"That is the way of it," said Osberne.

"Then," said the chief, "it must be that there is some evil spirit in this stuff, wherefore we had best rid ourselves of it.

Otherwise the evil may come upon us, and our men may play like some evil animal that cannot eat all that he has, nor will let the one who needs to eat, eat."

"Hail, Chief!" shouted some of the men, then stood and lifted their lances and gave the salute, booming out the chief's name thrice, "Amelkima! Amelkima! Amelkima!"

"Bring then all this yellow stuff which our brother and friend Ota-bben calls gold," the chief commanded. "Bring the stones he calls rubies. Kenu and another shall carry it all down to the ships; and I, Amelkima, shall give it to the men of the ships. But tomorrow, with the sun, I shall return."

Then the boys and girls took their gold and rubies, and the rings and ornaments, and threw them on to a guanaco skin. Some brought black and shining stones which they had found in the mountains, of no worth but good to see. Others cast in arrow heads of fine shape, small as peas, not made for hunting but for toys. Girls brought mats made of feathers of many colors, scarlet and white and blue and yellow and green-gold, edged with other feathers light as air. And when all had been brought, Kenu and the man Cama rolled up the hide with the treasure and thrust a stick through the ends, then lifted the burden on their shoulders and set off, the chief Amelkima walking behind them. As was the custom, the men ran forward, then ranged themselves into two lines, holding their lances crossed like an arch under which the burden-bearers and the chief walked. Coming out at the end of the arch the chief stopped and raised his lance, then called out in a strong voice, "Ma-ee-ya, ompa-ya!" which meant "Farewell companions!"

In a single voice the companions shouted heartily, "Ma-ee-ya, Amelkima! Ma-ee-ya, ompa-ya!" In that manner they always bade each other farewell.

But in the morning the three did not return at sun-up, which all thought strange, because with that folk a promise was a promise and a word a word. So Nio, the far-sighted, went up a hill to look, for from that high place he could see far down the valley, then over low hills, and beyond to the sea. Soon he came down and told how he had seen no sight of the chief and the two bearers, but had seen boats going from the ships to the shore, with many men in them. Then Osberne's heart sank with shame, for he feared treachery of some sort on the side of his own people. So also did Ato, who, seeing his companion's sorrowful face, felt something of the grief and fear that he felt, and grieved the more knowing how Osberne hated the evil deeds done by the men of the fleet.

" Hear me! I do not trust the men of the ship in such a case," cried Osberne. " We did wrong to send the gold. It would have been better to have cast it into the sea. The demon of greed may have been awakened and the end no man can guess. Let us go down to the ships, and know that I am with you in all."

So down they went, forty of them, with lances and arrows, not laughing and singing as was usual with them, but stern and somewhat sad.

When they came out from among the little hills and on to the plain that swept down to the sea-beach, Osberne knew that the day would be a sad one. For coming up, all of them with weapons, were men-at-arms, and their leader he knew to be Diego de Barrasa, a surly fellow and loud-mouthed and quarrelsome.

" God send that there be no fighting," said Osberne to Ato. " But it looks ugly." Then he turned to the Indians and begged them to stand and turn their lances point downwards as sign of peace, which they did.

But Diego, the leader of the men-at-arms, came running, and shouting, " Yield! Surrender! Dogs of Indians." One man let fly an arrow which came near Ato and which he caught with his hand, a trick practised by all the Indians and done easily as a man catches a ball, or easier, an arrow past its first swiftness lacking the speed of a ball.

Then a wild thought leaped up in Osberne's mind.

" Diego! " he shouted. " If fight there is to be let it be between us. Man and man we shall meet, with steel, or bow, or staff. What thou wilt. Let the best man win and these others go without blood-shedding."

" Dog and traitor and friend of savages! " shouted Diego. Then came a burst of shouts from the rest.

" Down with the Indian dogs! "

" Give us your gold! "

" Up, all, and end them! "

Then stones began to fly, thrown by the men of the fleet, and also a few arrows were let among the Indians, but doing no harm to them. So Osberne leaped forward, his hand held high for all to see, and he cried aloud, " Shed no blood, men! These are your friends! They have fed you and helped! " But still the armed men came running, some cursing, some waving their hands, some letting fly an arrow at random. Seeing that, Ato signed to the Indians who spread themselves in a long line making part of a circle, but with space between each man and his fellow for safety's sake. It seemed as though every sailor and man-at-arms shouted commands. Then from one of the ships a bombard roared like thunder, and when Osberne looked he saw other boats coming, full of armed men.

" Come to us as prisoner and you shall have mercy! " cried out Diego.

" I ask no mercy, but fair play, for these my friends," called Osberne.

" Shoot every dog here! " roared Diego, and then arrows began to fly thick. But to hit an Indian with an arrow was like trying to strike a cat with a stick. For they leapt aside, and flung themselves on the ground to rise again, and dropped their heads, but still went on with their sharp lances leveled. Then Osberne ran forward, leaped at Diego, and, by a wrestling trick threw him on the ground; and others came, so that blows rained on the lad and he was dragged and half carried down the beach and away from the Indians.

Then the battle was on, for Ato and his friends came at a run, not shooting for fear that they might wound Osberne, but running in close so that the men-at-arms could not use their bows. Also the Indians were not used to the killing of men. But they used their lances like staves, beating the men-at-arms about the head and body, making a great onslaught, so that many a man who had laid deep schemes to go back to the ship with a load of gold was satisfied to fly with a broken skin. In the middle of the crowd Osberne and Diego rolled about on the ground, close locked, each trying to get at the other's throat, but with Osberne not getting the best of matters because of his enemy being cased with breastplate and throat piece, while the lad was bare from the waist up. At one time Osberne had Diego well down and the soldier cried out for mercy.

" Tell me where is the chief, and the boy, and the other Indian! " demanded Osberne, and between gasps Diego said, " They fled to the hills." Then a blow fell on Osberne's wounded shoulder that made him well-nigh yell with pain, and next he was down and Diego uppermost, pressing the life out of him and choking him. Above and all about men scrambled and fought. He saw Ato fighting against two. He heard a blast of shouts and caught sight of a man with a poniard who had blood madness in his eyes, so Osberne struggled fiercely to get free knowing that the blow was to be aimed at him. But Ato leaped across as Osberne got to his knees, then many men leaped and ran, some over him, striking and kicking him so that the lad was all in a daze. How it came about that the poniard came down, not in him but in Diego's side, Osberne never knew. But soon a great cry went up, "Osberne has slain Diego! Osberne has slain Diego!" Then when the lad found his mind clear again there were the sailors and men-at-arms running down the beach to the boats, and Ato and the Indians were standing together, talking.

"This man was killed by one of his own fellows by mistake. I saw it," said Ato.

"A sad piece of work, Ato," said Osberne. "And the fleet will not believe but that I did it. But as soon as we find the chief and the boy, I shall go aboard and set things straight. The load will be heavy, I fear."

So a few Indians picked up the body and carried it to a clean place, then Osberne crossed the hands of it on the breast, and so they went away.

Now all the rest of that day they hunted the hills for the chief and the two Indians, believing Diego when he had told Osberne that they had gone to the north. They sought in the night too, spreading themselves in a long line and going back and forth so that no foot of land might be unseen. They did all that because some, remembering what the chief had said about an evil spirit in the gold, thought that by witchery a madness had been brought to Amelkima.

So the morning came, and with a sad heart Osberne took leave of Ato and his companions, telling them that he must go to the fleet, even if his death should follow on a false charge of stirring up the Indians and killing Diego. "And it grieves me to leave you," he said, "because never shall I see a better or a fairer land, nor more happy companions. So my love and friendship must stay with you."

"But why go to your death?" asked Ato.

"The day's work lieth before me, and that no man may deny," answered Osberne, sadly enough.

"Then," said Ato, "we shall go with you to the sea and bear witness to the men of the ship that you have done no wrong in this matter. That much I shall be able to make clear. Or I shall offer my life for yours."

Osberne smiled with heavy heart hearing that, knowing how little Ato's words would avail, or how little his offer be worth. But he was glad of the companionship, so they all went together, a great party of them, though at the hilltop the most of them stayed, and only Ato and four went down to the sea by way of a crooked valley, so crooked that they could not see the bay until they came out within a short distance of the water's edge.

At first sight of the bay Osberne's heart went to beating, and as for Ato, he was like one crazed with joy, for the bay was empty and the ships had gone, and out to sea, under a brisk wind, were four sails, far away and small.

"Is it grief you feel that you stand so?" asked Ato.

"I would that every man of the ships felt happy as I," answered Osberne. "But I have another fear."

"I know what it is," said Ato, "and that fear I too hold. It is that they have taken our chief and the boy and the other man."

"It is," answered Osberne.

"It will be easy to know," went on Ato. "We shall search the sea sands and find signs to tell us."

But soon they came upon something that set them to wondering still more. For, being on the top of the slope that ran down to the sea, they beheld two men, one tall and good-looking and dressed in armor; the other in a brown robe. The two of them stood looking out to sea.

When the two on the shore heard the Indians coming, which was not until a few lance lengths parted them, because of the noise of the sea, they turned, and Osberne knew them to be Cartagena and the priest Pedro. But though the two thought them to be enemies, Cartagena showed no fear, but laid his hand on his sword and half drew it. The priest made the sign of the cross. So Osberne called aloud, saying, "It is I. It is Osberne of Portsdown. And these are my friends."

For a moment it looked as if the knight might let fall the outside of him and be friendly, but instead, he said, proudly, "The ship boy who went with Indians. I have heard something of him. You know this land well?"

Then uprose in Osberne the old spirit, that in which he talked with Sir Robert in Portsdown one hour, or with the innkeeper another, or with some traveler another. "Juan de Cartagena —"

"Captain Juan de Cartagena," corrected the knight.

"For your men, yes. But where are your men? I, too, am captain, or I was. Now I am as you, one who knows less of the land than these Indians, my friends. So let us throw aside the trimmings and titles and stand four-square. Neither pedigrees nor titles avail here."

Juan de Cartagena looked at Osberne with his hawk's eye for a space, then laughed.

" What manner of country is it, Osberne? " he asked.

" A good land, because a land of peace," was the reply.

" Shall a man starve? "

" If he knows not enough to catch his own food."

" Can I get an Indian to guide me? "

" Not as man to master, but as friend, perhaps."

" I have gold enough to pay for service."

" But service is not to be bought," answered Osberne. " And gold is nothing."

" And you? What shall you do? " asked the knight.

" How can I know when I do not know why I have been left behind; nor, when I think of it, do I know why you are left behind."

Osberne could see that the knight was plucking up heart to cast aside his pride and be with him as man to man, and he knew that the struggle was no light one. But he also knew that the best way to a man's heart is by the road of the belly, so he spoke to Ato and told him somewhat of how things were, saying that the knight was a chief who had no followers, and that the loss sat upon him heavily. Ato, on his part, could not see why the knight should be sorrowful at being in that land instead of on the ship. However, he and Osberne, with one or two helping, went to work and spread a meal on the grass under some stunted willows by the stream. Then they all sat down, well prepared to eat, though the knight shifted himself so as to sit between the priest and Osberne and away from the

Indians. But the meal brought them ten leagues nearer together in understanding.

But long before the knight and the priest had ended their meal, the Indians had scattered, going along the beach looking at the tracks and knowing much by what they saw, so only Ato sat with the three.

" When you fought on the beach and killed Diego — " began the knight.

" Kill him I did not," said Osberne. " He died in the fight but by whose dagger I do not know."

" That is as I thought and hoped," said the priest, very gravely.

" Then let me say that while the fight went on we sent men ashore in the boats to help against the Indians, believing that all the savages in the land had come to avenge the three Indians who brought the gold."

" Avenge? Do not say that they are dead," said Osberne.

" Not dead but prisoners on the ships."

" But why prisoners? " asked Osberne.

" Magellan took them as presents to the king."

" A most foul piece of work," said Osberne.

" But kings have always looked for savages from new lands," said the knight. " I see nothing amiss in that. All conquerors have brought captives to prove their victories, and sometimes those captives have been willing men in captivity. There is Enrique, Magellan's slave, with him on this voyage."

" But these they took came with gifts," said Osberne.

" It was their gifts that betrayed them," said the priest. " Where there is gold, there the devil dwells. Gold is the devil's fishhook as some say."

" The sight of all that gold set the men on fire," went on the knight. "You should have heard them. One man said he knew that there were caves full of gold and rubies. Another spoke of hidden treasure. Pigafetta, the writing man, went about telling of Prester John and his riches. So, with none able to speak the Indian tongue the fools began to question, shouting at the strangers as is the manner of men who cannot make themselves understood, and taking the silence of the tall chief for secret knowledge."

"When he flung out his arm, meaning that he would go ashore, then they took the sign for showing where the gold lay," said the priest, " so they began to ask him to guide them there. Then Espinosa, seeing the chief quiet, and taking that for fear, struck him in the mouth, but by sheer weight and stature he sent Espinosa spinning across the deck with a movement of his arm."

"But Magellan. What of him? Had he no part in it?" asked Osberne.

"A strange man of many moods, never two hours the same," answered the knight. "He stood looking and listening. When the men spoke of torture to make the Indians confess their hiding place where the gold lay, one shouting for the rack, another for thrusting splinters between finger-nail and flesh, another for thrusting burning brands in their faces — then Magellan said his say. 'What force cannot, cleverness may,' he said. Magellan showed honey but mixed poison. He ordered the men to bring gifts, which they did; looking-glasses, and bells, and knives that would not cut, and all such trash. So they loaded the arms and hands of the Indians until the things were piled high. That was Magellan's honey. But all the while the chief stood, a proud man, much as a kind soul might receive gifts of no worth from a child

who did not understand. But treachery was afoot. It was
Magellan's poison. For there came men with chains and hammers, and other men chosen for their strength. They seized
the Indians and threw them down on the deck, and the smiths
clapped iron rings on their hands and feet, then riveted and
chained them, heeding it not at all that they bruised them.
So they were taken to the hold, two on Magellan's ship and one
to the *San Antonio,* and more miserable men it would be hard
to find."

Osberne rose to his feet, red with anger.

"Now I swear," he said, "that I will not rest until I have
found the ships and set my friends free! There must be a way
in this strait to reach the ships, and I shall steal the prisoners
who are my friends away to their own place. I am ashamed
of the men of my own race."

He stopped short, choked with fury.

"Master thy anger," counseled the priest. "A man in a
passion rides a horse that runs away with him."

"But I know these people," said Osberne after a while, somewhat cooler. I had sooner put my faith in the chief, or in the
boy, or in Ato here, or in any of these, my Indian friends, than
in Magellan, or any of his captains and officers. Liars and
black-hearted scoundrels they are. Their trades are stealing
and murder."

Then Ato spoke, laying his right hand on Osberne's left
shoulder and looking straight into his friend's eyes. "There
can be no missing the ships," he said. "They must go by a
crooked way and we by a straight. They will stop here and
stop there, and winds may beset them. They must go south.
They must go to the setting sun. Then they must go north
again. We can have them at twenty places."

Turning what Ato said into speech that Cartagena and the priest could understand somewhat cooled Osberne. He remembered that he knew nothing of why the two had been set ashore and it troubled him that he had not asked. So he put a question to know.

"Magellan dared not kill me as he did those he defeated in the mutiny," said Cartagena. "I was made co-admiral with him by the king. But he must have his revenge though, and like the pope's mule he kept his kick for seven years. Mark then how he compassed my death. Seeing all that had been done to these Indians and that they would rise up, he set me ashore. This good priest chose to come with me, giving up his life if need be for his friend. That is the tale of it."

"And what shall you do now?" asked Osberne.

"There are things working out," answered Cartagena. "The *San Antonio* will give the fleet the slip in the straits and return to Spain. It is all well planned. The ship's captain has promised to put in here and take us home. As I say it all clears well, the better since these Indians are not blood-thirsty savages to fall on us and eat us. So here we shall wait until they come, and if some of the Indians will give us food, then we ask no more."

"So treachery and mutiny still work in the fleet," said Osberne.

"As peaceful men you must throw away your arms," advised Ato. "Fear not that our people shall do you harm. Lift no hand against them and they will lift no hand against you. Go about like this good man you call priest, not with pride but quiet."

"And if you stay here, then shall we be glad," said Cartagena.

"Not so. I go with Ota-bben, my companion," said Ato. "We must free the chief, and Kenu, and Cama."

"But there will be time for you to do something for our comfort," said the knight.

"Not so. We shall start now," said Ato and, putting his fingers to his mouth gave a loud and shrill whistle, hearing which the Indians who were scattered about the beach commenced running.

"You go thus, unprepared?" asked Cartagena of Osberne.

"There is naught to prepare," Osberne answered. "Food lies all about us. There are no enemies to cut throats. One sleeps where night finds him. A man wakes at dawn, ready. There are neither knaves nor fools nor murderers in the land."

"I can scarcely blame you then for loving a land where men are not as snarling beasts," said Cartagena. "But surely you take men to carry things, food and clothes and gear."

Osberne laughed a little. "The madness of owning things has long since gone from me," he said. "As a boy I learned the prayer that asked for daily bread, but worried much for things I thought I wanted. I have since learned that it is better for a man to want what he cannot have than to have what he does not want."

"But surely a sword and a breastplate," said the knight.

"The sword is useless for there is no man to kill, and with a sword you cannot hunt. A breastplate is a folly and hindrance. It would hamper in running, burden in walking, and would be a cold comfort at night. But I thank you."

"Then," said the knight, "as you will find the *San Antonio* in some place, as this Ato says, why should not we go with you, hiding until a proper time."

"Now it seems hard to say," answered Osberne, "but your

way of life has not fitted you for such a venture. You would hinder us in that which we have to do. You have not learned to make your own living. You are soft and cannot run. You have not been useful to yourself but have leaned on others. So you would lean on us. Now that is the truth though it hurts. And when we see the *San Antonio* we shall tell them how we left you."

After that there was little time for talk. The Indians who had come at Ato's whistle talked among themselves, and Osberne listened. When they understood, from Ato's tale, the sad manner of the capture of their chief and the two, and were told that the work of rescue lay ahead, then all were eager to go. But after counsel only six went, and they were chosen for reasons. Nio of the keen eyes was one. Macho, called the quiet, was chosen because of the way he could creep about, quiet as a field-mouse in the darkest night, making no noise. Tenka the strong also was chosen; also Rolda-aka than whom no man was a better swimmer. Baka the swift-footed was the fifth, and Nato, who sometimes lived with the canoe Indians, was the sixth, for he was one who never rested, but must needs go from place to place to know how things and people were.

"All will go well," shouted Osberne, as the eight companions went away, but the face of Cartagena showed no high hope.

"They are as children afraid to be alone," said Ato, and after that both Cartagena and the priest were clean forgotten by the Indian.

So they started, nor is there much to tell of the first part of the journey. It was a stout and well ordered little company, all of them friendly, all of them tall and strong, all of them happy-faced, and when the eight gained the hilltop they raised their

lances aloft and shouted a last farewell to their companions and
Cartagena and his companion on the beach. They laughed
merrily as they went. They went on the live-long day and
slept where night found them. They awoke betimes and were
on the trail before the sun rose. They killed no more food than
they needed and each morning ate enough to last for the day,
and if luck favored them toward evening they hunted in la-
goon, or in valley, getting duck or goose or other wild fowl.
And Nio of the keen eyes, and Baka who knew every foot of
the country were leaders.

Between low mountains lay their course for three days, and
after that they came to a magic sea of tall grass, then to gray
barren uplands, then to where the grass grew scantier until
they came to a desert plain, then the desert changed to barren
sand hills. One day the way was rough and painful, for they
had to cross a tract where nothing grew, and where the ground
was a hard and glassy rock which had flowed from a burning
mountain as Bako said. Then once more they came to grass,
and plains with tree clumps, and one day to a high place from
which they looked down on a strait of sea water, and on the
other side stretched another land. To their left hand, as they
stood facing the south, lay a great bay-like opening and still
further beyond that the sea with breaking white waves. To
their right lay another opening. So did Osberne come to look
upon the straits through which the ships must pass, and it was
eighteen days after they had left the Bay of San Julian. But
more than forty days passed before the ships came to the straits,
though some of the company always stayed there on watch.

Sometimes Nio the quick-eyed and one or two companions
went north to see what there was to see, and once they met a
party of Indians who had seen the ships at anchor where the

Santiago's skeleton lay, the men picking up and taking aboard the ships what they could find. Another time Osberne and Ato and Rolda-aka walked to the west and met a party of Indians in a canoe. So the three embarked with their new-found friends and they rowed into the straits and came to an island where they stayed for two days. Never had Osberne seen the like for geese and ducks, and those other strange birds that do not fly but swim in the sea, which he afterwards knew as penguins. There were seals too, and sea-lions which had no fear of the Indians, nor had the Indians of them. And in one place on the island there were small white birds so many that when they rose from the ground it was like a cloud flying over and darkening the sun. But Osberne taught his Indian friends a new trick that pleased them greatly, for he fashioned a sail out of the thin skin of young guanacos, and a mast from two stout lances lashed together, so that in a light breeze they sailed, to everyone's delight. To be sure there were mishaps, and with the sudden wind the canoe ofttimes turned over, but that mattered not at all, the Indians being like ducks in the water, strong and brave swimmers.

One day Nio the quick-eyed, who was on watch, called out that the ships were in sight, so all ran to the hilltop and there saw them in the bay. The *Trindad* and the *Victoria* dropped anchor, but the *Concepcion* and the *San Antonio* sailed through the narrows and into the second bay, and there Osberne looked down upon the ships on the water, seeing the men like dolls and the ships themselves like children's toys.

CHAPTER VIII

The Patagonians

TO SHOW how narrow the strait is where Osberne and his companions overlooked it from the headland, and to show how the headland is a point from which one may see far to east and to west, there is this. Not many years after Magellan passed through, the explorer Sarmiento went from west to east, and, seeing the same good vantage point, wrote to his king that the best way to keep out the pirate Drake would be to hang chains across the strait at that place.

" Here they must pass," said Baka, pointing to the narrow way. " From this place Nio could see the ships sailing the ocean before the men on the ships knew they were at the straits."

So it was. They saw the four ships sail into the strait. They saw two of them drop anchor and the other two go forward timidly, then pass so close under their eyes that they could look down on the decks and see the men going back and forth, and the man on watch, and the bell boy striking the bell, and the captains walking up and down, and the man in the foretop. They saw the *Concepcion* and the *San Antonio* pass into the second bay, then sail from north to south and from south to north again, and after that swing down into the second narrow place and come back with the tide and anchor in the shelter of the headland on which the companions stood. So the companions left their watching-place and went down nearer to the ships, but keeping out of sight, and staying on the land side of a low hill. Near to that hill was a shallow opening of the sea, not to be seen from the ships, and in that creek lay a canoe.

In the morning the tide set bad for the ships and there was no wind, so the sea lay smooth and still. Peeping over the ridge of the hill, the companions saw a boat coming ashore, then Nio and Baka stood up in full sight, knowing what would happen. And happen it did, for no sooner had the boatmen seen the two figures than a man who sat by the steersman tried a shot at them which fell short. But there was also this. They heard one shout, and Osberne knew him to be the mate. It was this, that he said, "Turn back, men. Back to the ships. There are savages and it may be an ambush." Thereupon the boats turned and went back in great hurry.

"And now," Osberne told his companions, "on board they will tell a great tale, and the writing man, Pigafetta, will set down how the fleet was attacked by giants. But the folly of them! To kill, and to kill, and to kill. It makes me sick at heart to see that madness for blood and for death."

"How easy it would be for us to gather enough men to put an end to all of them, ships and men," said Baka. "Came they to land for food, then we could capture them, one by one.

Soon they would starve on their ships, fearing to come to land."

"But then our three companions would die with them, for the shipmen would not set them free," said Nio.

"It would please me well to go on the ships at night," said Macho. "I would go quiet and quick as a bird, Tenka going with me. He could break the chains. Or not breaking the chains then Rolda-aka could swim back with our friends."

Osberne thought about that for a time. "The doing of that would be well enough if you knew the ways of ships," he said. "But the inside of a ship is worse than a fox hole, all corners and hidden places, all dark and locked. The belly of a ship is not an open place like a canoe. There are doors, and there are keys, many of them, and one must know. Now if I could go on the ship it would be an easier task. Nor do I think they would know me for what I am, but would take me for a Patagonian. It would be good sport to make the venture, all of us, not secretly and in the night, but openly in the day, seeing and hearing. Who would be for such a venture?"

"All of us," said Ato. "Nor would they know us to be the same they saw at San Julian. They know not one of us from another."

"Almost blind and unseeing as bats, they are, the shipmen," said Nio. "But then it is small wonder, because on the ships there is only a little way to look, except at sea, then they look not close. They have lost the sight of their eyes not using them, much as a man never walking would lose the use of his legs."

"But how shall it be for understanding?" asked Tenka the strong.

"They will shout. They will wave their arms. They will

make faces," said Nio. "Thus do all white strangers, as if noise made for understanding," he added.

"There is a fool on the ship nearest," Osberne told them. "He has a name for making Patagonians understand, yet he speaks not a word of any tongue but his own, and that badly. The captain will order him to tell us this and that and he will shout and wave his arms, as Nio says, nor will there be any meaning to it. But he will tell the captain things out of his head and what he says I shall hear, and tell you. But none of us must laugh. And I think we shall fool them and maybe learn something of those we would rescue."

"But there is no time to lose," said Nato. "Signs are that a wind will come at noon, and a great one. And if these ships are not to be driven ashore here then they must go to other side, against the Land of Fire."

"Then," said Osberne, "maybe we shall get a great name as medicine-men, foretelling the storm."

"Let us make ready," said Nio, so they went to work, striping themselves with lines of red and yellow and black and white, until they were so changed that one hardly knew his fellow. About their foreheads they bound fillets of fur, and stuck ostrich feathers in their hair so that they looked tall above the run of men, and their long guanaco cloaks made them look taller. They took neither bows nor arrows but only their lances. Then Osberne hid in his hair a piece of gold about the size of the top of a man's thumb. "It may be that the captain will bow low before this," he told the others. "Or again it may unlock a door. Many a prison door flies open with a golden key. We shall see."

In merry mood they went to the canoe and set it in the water, then paddled out to the nearest ship, which was the *Concep-*

cion. When they drew near, they saw on the decks and looking over the side, many armed men. Juan Sebastian del Cano,
big and burly and masterful, the captain of the ship, stood
somewhat apart from the rest.

Osberne heard him call out to Roldan de Argote, the gunner,
to have all ready to shoot, if need be, so warned his companions
to keep a sharp eye open, then slip in the water and swim under
water at the first sign of danger. " But," he told them, " there
is little fear. These bowmen are poor marksmen, being men
of the city for the most part, who would starve if they had to
lean on their shooting for their food."

When the canoe lay alongside not an Indian moved, and all
held their arms crossed on their chests with their hands showing so that those on the ship could see they had no weapons except the lances. Those lay in a bundle in the canoe.

Osberne heard the mate, Juan de Acurio, say to the captain,
" It is certain that these know nothing of San Julian. Indeed
there is no way for them to pass news. They cannot write and
they have no horses, being poor folk and stupid."

Then the captain said, " We shall treat them fair because
we know not what lies before us in these strange straits. And
see to it that the old savage in irons knows nothing of these
being here, or he may set them against us because of the San
Julian matter."

Osberne told his companions all that, and they sat silent as if
full of wonder at the ship. In ending, Osberne said to his
companions, as if he had been speaking of the ships in wonder, " Now comes the man gifted in sign language. He will
wave and shout and seem angry, and he believes that strangers
to his tongue understand the better because of great noise.
Now he begins."

" Come ye in peace? " bawled the mate, then as sign of what he asked he threw his arms about a page named Pedro.

" His sign looks as if he would choke the lad to death," said Nato, in high good humor, after Osberne had told them what the mate said.

" Or that he hungers and would eat the boy," said Baka.

" One might take it to mean that he wants to get his hands on us," said Tenka.

" Now you shall hear me," said Baka the swift-footed. " But it would go ill if they understood." So he stood up in the canoe and said, in a mild voice, as if he flattered and praised the strangers, " O man of the many signs that deceive, yet do not deceive. We know you to be fools and traitors and false fellows." Then he looked to his companions and asked, " What say ye? "

They chanted, rolling out the Indian words finely, keeping up the sport, " We know you to be fools and traitors and false fellows."

Baka went on.

" We come to look for our stolen companions. We come to steal them back. We come to make fools of you." As he spoke he pointed and traced lines in the air, then threw his hands apart, thereby meaning nothing at all. At the end he lifted a spear and gave it to the page, with the point at his own breast.

" What says the fellow? " asked Juan Sebastian. " Make you aught of the silly chatter? "

" It is plain as the day," answered the mate. " I have enough of the Indian talk to come by what he says. He tells us that he is sent as messenger from their king. He offers us the spear with the point to his breast meaning that he

offers you his life knowing you to be a great ruler. He believes you to be a king of might and of many banners. He
says further — "

"Ask him if his people are loyal to the King of Spain and
will swear allegiance. When that is done tell him that we
come to take possession of this land and all its ports, and its
districts, without opposition, for our most Catholic and very
powerful king."

The mate scratched his head, hearing that. "It is not an
easy thing to put into the sign language," he said. "Still, I
learned much from a man who sailed with Columbus and
knew these Indians." Then he shouted, "Are you loyal to
the King of Spain?" and, to make them understand and to
put all clearly he thrust his hands by the side of his head with
his fingers spread, to show a crown as Osberne supposed
and told his friends, though he could hardly keep his face
straight. The mate went on with his signs, showing loyalty
to the King of Spain by laying his hand on his stomach and
bowing.

"His sign might mean that he is hungry," said Ato.

"Or that he has eaten penguin and feels sick," added Baka.

"Where a man feels pain there he lays his hand," said Nio.

"To work then and follow me," said Osberne. So they all
put their right hands to their bellies and bowed. Then they
did as the mate had done with his hands, making what Baka
called "guanaco's ears."

"If I cannot laugh my sides must crack," said Rolda-aka.
"Oh, a merry tale this will be to tell."

"They take it to mean that from this time you do not belong to yourselves. You give yourselves, and all this land, and
all your people, and the mountains and rivers and animals and

birds to their master, the king," said Osberne. " But quiet. I want to hear what they say on the ship."

What Osberne heard was nothing but praise of the mate Juan, and his skill in sign language.

" He understands the savages as we do one another," said one.

" He is clear to them as water," said another.

" Teach me the sign language and how to do thus and so," said another.

" Ask them their names," put in a ship boy.

But the captain came in with, " Tell them to come aboard, bringing no weapons."

So the mate began to turn his hand about, wheel-fashion, saying the while, " Come on board and fear nothing. We are your best friends."

" We shall trust you as the guanaco trusts the hungry lion," said Osberne, but in the Indian tongue.

" He says that they are peaceful," said the mate, whereupon the companions climbed on board.

" Now," said Osberne to the Indians, " we shall see a merry game. They hold us as of no understanding while they stand on the top-most peak of wisdom. But first let us give a message to our chief, Amelkima." So he began to chant, and the rest followed, all singing loud:

Happily we will look on you, O Chief.
We know you are near us.
We know you hear us.
We know you are bound.
We know that we shall see you again.
You shall walk in the sun.
You shall sit by the river.

You shall see your people.
You shall be free again where the winds blow.
Far off they have taken you but we are here.
We follow you and your captors.
We have prepared a way for your freedom.
Give no sign, O Chief.
Give your enemies no word.
Happily we will look on you, O Chief, before many days.

"Can you make that out?" asked Captain Juan.

"More than half of it," answered the mate. "They sing to their spirit calling on him to be with them."

"Then, Roldan de Argote, get ready your cannon and let them hear the roar of it so that they shall know something of our power," commanded the captain. Thereupon the gunner, with some others, went to work preparing a piece of artillery, loading it with powder but not ball.

"Now," said Osberne to his friends, "we shall have great sport. They think that you have never heard that bellowing. They still believe us to be fools, knowing nothing and fearing everything."

"What does he say?" asked the captain. "Give ear."

"They are amazed at what they see," the mate answered. "They look upon us as gods."

"Now, Tenka," said Osberne, "there is the cannon. You see how many of them it takes to move it. They would push it to the opening. . . Show them what you can do. The amazements should not be all on one side."

Thereupon Tenka went to the cannon, set his arms and breast to it, and pushed it to the place with ease. So the gunner and his men stood open mouthed.

"If all of them are of such strength in the lands bordering

these straits, we must have a care," said the gunner. "It will not do to play with such giants, for giants in strength they are."

"Then we shall show our strength," said the captain. "Make your noise, Roldan."

"Now you are to tremble," said Osberne.

"They know not how we have heard the thunders in the mountains," said Ato. He added, "Be ready, Tenka."

"Great shall be my fear as you shall see," said Tenka.

With a flourish the gunner set a match to the touch hole and the gun roared. Thereupon, as though frightened at the noise and supposing it to be some wild animal, Tenka and Baka leaped forward and seized the cannon. Next Tenka lifted it and raised it high above his head and threw it into the sea. Then he took the barrel of powder and cast that into the water. It was a show of strength that made the seamen gasp. But only the gunner stepped forward to scold the Patagonian, though he had no chance to say a word. For Ato and Osberne, as if in half-anger, laid hands on Tenka and pushed him away among his companions. Then Osberne took the piece of gold out of his hair where it had lain hidden, and, holding it up for all to see, offered it to del Cano, saying, in a loud voice, for his companions to hear, while the seamen wondered at it as a speech of peace offering, "You fool! Because of your folly you have lost a gun. It is safe where it will do no more harm."

"It is a peace offering that he offers," said the mate.

"It would buy two such guns," said the gunner.

"Save us from fighting against such giants," said the barber Hernando.

"Gold can make them blind and forgiving," said Ato.

"Before gold a king will take off his hat," added Osberne for his companions to hear.

Sebastian del Cano took the gold and overlooked the loss of his cannon and gunpowder. " Is there more of this in the land? " he asked. " Ask them, Juan, in your sign language."

So the mate, hard put to it to invent, took a small chest and made motions as if gathering up something and putting it in the box, then acted as if he could get the lid closed only by standing on it. All the time he shouted, " Mucho oro? Mucho oro? " meaning, " plenty gold! "

By way of making answer, Ato stretched his hands to the land and made motions as if filling the ship's hold with gold. Thereupon the men brought out their trading things, their looking-glasses and little bells and red caps, offering them, but not an Indian would look at them.

" One would think that they feared some such trick as we played on the three at San Julian," Osberne heard a seaman named Gomez say to Hernando the barber.

" I wish that the captain would bring up the old man from below," said the barber.

" It might not be ill to do so," said the mate, and spoke to the captain.

" There can be no harm," said del Cano. " These savages have no way of writing letters. They have no horses. And we are far from San Julian. It would be well to see how they greet one another. So bring him up."

" Now comes the time," said Osberne to Ato. " Let none speak or give sign. And surely the chief will give no sign."

So two seamen went below and soon returned with the tall, old chief who looked noble in his white hair, and who carried himself erect, though his hands were chained. Osberne and his companions chanted again,

Give no sign, O Chief.
Give your enemies no word.

And the chief stood looking at the Indians as he might have looked at a tree, no sign of knowing them in his eyes. Nor did they give any sign of having seen him before.

" It is certain that they know not one another," said Roldan to the mate.

" Now," said Osberne, " it is time that we did our magic. We shall foretell the storm that is coming. These know nothing of it because the skies in this land are not as the skies in theirs. There a storm does not leap out of a clear sky."

Osberne went near to where the captain and the mate stood, but not too near lest they should be suspicious. Then he bowed low, with his hand laid on his heart, so the mate made a guess, saying, " He would have speech with you, Captain. It may be that he will offer to guide us to the gold."

But Osberne, keeping his ears pricked, heard much talk among the sailors.

One said, " We should not let these go."

Another said, " Fellows of such strength would work the ship well."

A third asked, " If we let them go how shall we come to know where the gold is? "

A fourth said, " Such fellows would bring good price in the slave market."

The mate said, " Captain, as we go back to the flagship, it would be well to take these as a present to the admiral."

" I have been thinking of that," del Cano answered. " Also that we may find other Indians in these straits, and if they attack us we can use these as hostages, or even offer to kill them

to save our own lives. But we must act secretly and with caution. In a little while let some one cut their canoe adrift. And
let others be ready with sticks to knock them on the head.
But let all act together. It is no light job to attack men who
can do with a cannon as these did." He said all smiling, and
turning his hand this way and that as if talking about the ship.
But Osberne told his companions all, and saw to it that the
chief also heard and understood. And as he did what he did
presently he said more, planning things, and telling what was
said by the seamen. So the Indians kept a look-out without
seeming to do so.

"Ask this Indian what he would tell us," said del Cano to
the mate.

So the mate touched his tongue and made foolish noises in
his throat. Then Osberne took two feathers and laid them on
the ship's deck. Next he marked out with his finger two lines
on the boards, drawing the coasts with all their points and their
bays so that the thickest-headed there might know what he
showed. Everything was shown, the narrows, the islands, all
that the seamen had seen. Next he moved the two feathers,
making the course that the ships had sailed in the straits.

"He is showing us the straits and the lay of them, and the
way we have gone," said the mate.

"Do you think me a fool to be told what I see before my
eyes?" asked the captain. "It seems to me that we need this
fellow for our navigation."

Then Osberne began to blow on the feathers, making the
wind come from the direction that the storm must come from,
not blowing in any rough fashion but enough to rock the
feathers.

"Now can he be foretelling a storm?" asked the barber.

"But the sky is clear," said the page Juan.

"I have been told that these savages have dealings with the evil one and can conjure a storm," said the gunner.

"But see how he draws the feathers across the strait," said Juan de Acuria, the mate. "As I live, if a storm came from the southeast, then that would be the only shelter where ships might lie safe."

Nio whispered, "Ota-bben, they have just sunk our canoe. And here men come with sticks and ropes."

Then Osberne stood up and pointed to the sky where a reddish black cloud was spreading. Already little eddies of wind made the flag flutter, now this way and now that.

"Stand out of here!" shouted the mate and men began to run about, some to get sail on the ship, others to capture the companions. But soon those last were flying for their lives, because the mighty Tenka uprose and tackled three of the knaves at once. One he sent overboard, one he thrust with a push halfway across the deck, the other, in high terror, fled into the rigging. After him went Swift-foot, up to the yards then to the top mast, where he stood a short while then dived into the sea, cutting the water clean, and striking out for land. Then Tenka ran to the chief and wrenched the chains apart that held him, and the old man took to the water, Rolda-aka on one side of him and Baka on the other. Next Nio dived. But Tenka had to have his joke, so, while he ran to the forecastle, he picked up a page on the way, making as if he would carry off the screaming fellow, but put him down unharmed. Then seeing three men struggling with the flapping tri-sail and making a poor job of it because of the growing wind, he must needs lend them a hand, wherefore it went up with a run. Nor did any lift a hand against him because of the stress everywhere, what with many things to do and the rising storm. The last three of the companions to dive into the sea were Ato and Tenka and Osberne, and great sport they made, shouting and splashing and laughing. But by the time they had gained the beach the two ships were well out in the straits, pitching and rocking because of the rising waves.

Thus did the companions rescue their chief, and his face was happy as his heart could make it when they climbed to the top of the headland where they could keep watch. The next day, when the storm had ended, they saw the two ships join Magellan's flagship, and heard the bombards roar a welcome.

On the day after the four ships lifted their anchors and set sail with a fair wind, to go through the straits, then the companions made new plans. The chief and Rolda-aka and Baka would stay on the headland to watch, while Osberne and Ato and Macho and Nato and Nio and Tenka would go by a short way to a place where the ships would anchor, not far from the South Sea. For the ships would have to sail many leagues, this way and that, but the companions could go by a way which Nato knew and so save many days.

" But," said Ato, " if the men on the ships grow faint-hearted, turning back, then Baka the swift-footed can find us and we shall meet at San Julian again, for there the ships would anchor and stop, before starting to cross the ocean."

Then Nato traced a chart to the straits in the dust and made all clear.

"In three days we shall be at a haven where the ships must stop, but it will take twenty days or more for them to get there," said Nato.

" There will be canoe folk, doubtless," said Osberne.

" We shall find some at the place where we touch the water,"
answered Nato. " They are fair folk. I know them well."

" We must somehow watch for the time when the ship called
the *San Antonio* deserts," added Osberne.

" Go and come back joyful," said the chief.

So they stood up, ready for the road at any time, and, having
saluted, the six set off together.

And it was a pleasant land through which they went, grassy
and with many a stream, and the day one with a bright sun.
In two full days they came to the sea that ran up into the land
and there met some of the people of Cayrayxaviisus, a fishing
folk who sailed about on that inland sea. They told the companions, as Nato had told them too, that there were many ways
between islands to the ocean, but all of them being narrow,
the ships would choose the main way. " For canoes such as
ours," said they, " many of the ways are easy, but for those who
do not know and who sail in such big ships there would be
griefs and perils what with rocks and winds, and twistings and
turnings." So they all ate and drank together by a clear spring
of water, then arose and pushed out their canoes and set forth,
all of them very joyous. At night they landed in their canoes
in the straits, by a noisy river full of little fish and where the sea
lay deep while all around were high mountains, a most proper
haven for ships, as Osberne saw.

Happy place though it was, yet neither Ato nor Osberne
could stay there waiting but must needs set forth on the straits
in canoes, to meet the ships or to watch them, as a fox watches a
bird. Nato too had to go because he knew the lay of the land
and the waters. Nor did the others willingly stay behind
though they agreed to do so, keeping watch lest the ships pass
that way, when they would somehow find Osberne and the

two with him. So having settled all that they waited for the dawn, hardly able to sleep.

OSBERNE never forgot those days of going about in a canoe. A party of the Cayrayxaviisus folk went with them in a second canoe. They raced, going so fast that the white water curved high on both sides of the prow. Sometimes they swam, making a noise that echoed again and again from the mountains, awakening sea-gulls, and sea-hens, and noisy ducks that came tumbling down the precipice and hastened across the beach, and half flew along the water making a wake like a canoe. They rowed up openings that ran far into the land, where high mountains all snow-tipped rose on both sides, and where it was still in air and on land and on water, and where a world lay mirrored in the blue-green sea. White albatrosses floated up the wind. They saw seals and sea-lions, so quiet and tame that they did not move, but watched the men with wondering brown eyes. There were little islands where they saw strange things of the sea, crabs, and sea-eggs, and starfish, and shells like jewels for daintiness. Once they left their canoes and climbed a mountain, tree-covered from the water's edge, and when they were so high that they could see the sea, and the winding straits, they found a river of ice. They came down again another way, by a steep slope, snow-covered, and made a merry time of it sliding down while the snow flew up like feathers.

The third day they rowed down the strait to a place where the hillsides grew more gentle and the hills lower, and at last came out to plain country again where the straits widened out like a great bay. It was there, many days later, that they saw the four ships part company, two going to the south, and two which they knew to be the flagship and the *Victoria* making

for the strait. So Osberne guessed that it would be well to follow the two that went south, which were the *Concepcion* and
the *San Antonio,* because it seemed certain that the other two
would anchor to await the coming of their consorts, and the
anchorage would be in the haven where the people of Cayrayxaviisus camped with Tenka and the others. Before the
two ships had sailed many leagues they parted company at an
island, one going one way, the other another, so the two canoes,
following like foxes, went the way of the *San Antonio,* which
sailed down an opening in the land which, as Nato said, and
he knew, had no outlet, wherefore the ship must presently turn
back. But that night the companions found much to befall
them.

From the *San Antonio* a boat went ashore when it was near
to evening, the place where they landed being a great bay, not
in Patagonia but on the shore of the Land of Fire. Now Osberne and his friends watched them, for they had their canoes
in a creek, so they could not be seen from the land. But in the
place where the boat landed, with five seamen, there lived Ona
Indians, a brave tribe of people, swift of foot and quick with
bow and arrow, none of whom had seen white men before.
One of them had slain a guanaco for meat that day, and the
flesh of it, properly cut up, hung in bushes, for the Ona folk
knew nothing of mine and thine among themselves, but what
belonged to one belonged to all, though not to any outside
the tribe except such a one should be hungry and in need, and
asked for food. Now what should happen, as Osberne and
Ato saw, but that the five seamen having seen the meat marked
it for their own, so went up the beach and began to take it
from where it hung. Then an Ona came down, very fearless,
and made to take the meat from the five seamen. That they

were five to his one he thought nothing of, nor would have hung back had they been twenty or fifty to his one. But a man-at-arms, hot tempered and hungry, took his sword and thrust at the Indian who leaped aside but caught at the blade with his two hands, knowing nothing of its sharpness, so the Indian was sorely hurt and his hands cut and bleeding. Thereupon he shouted something at which many of the tribe came running, and seeing the hurt, and learning the way of it, were angry at the seamen and especially at the man-at-arms. So there rose high words which the seamen took for threatenings, though they were only explanations and warnings; and in the middle of it all the man-at-arms slashed with his sharp sword at the head of one of the Indians, who drew back, but not quick enough, for part of his cheek was sorely slashed. Then the Onas flashed into anger, and a gallant sight it was to see them surround the seamen and hold them in spite of the kickings and shoutings, then carry them up the beach and over a sand hill and out of sight. As for those on the ship, seeing all that trouble and thinking to strike fear into the Indians, they began firing bombards and shooting shafts, though all of the last fell into the sea, and the balls from the cannon buried themselves in the sand.

"Now it will be easy to tell these Onas how things are and to set the sailors free," said Nato. "I know these people for good folk, but a sort not to be trampled on. What say you if we go to them?"

And that the others were willing to do.

So Osberne and Ato and Nato went running up the beach and soon came to the camp where they saw more than a hundred Onas, and the five seamen sitting on the ground, most miserable, and, lo, and behold! one of them was Hans. But the

Ona Indians made no move to hurt the three, seeing them to be people of their own kind and not unfriendly, for Osberne and his two friends held their hands high in sign of peace. Then Nato told the Indians how things were, and what they were doing there, and the manner of men the seamen and men-at-arms were, killing and destroying in season and out of season.

Hearing the story the chief said, " Then it will be well to put such vermin out of the way. We should call our people who will come from far and wide, Indians of the canoes too, and there will be little left of these destroyers in a short while."

" Not so," said Ato. " Even now they have enough, what with fightings among themselves, and with hunger, and with thirst; and, as you shall soon see, they will leave and go to their own place, coming here no more."

So the Indians talked with one another until the anger of the Onas had passed somewhat. Then Osberne came forward and Nato told about him, and how he loved the Indians and the life they led, and how he asked that one of the prisoners be given to him, because Osberne wanted to take Hans aside and talk with him privately, the rest of the seamen knowing nothing of what went on. When the chief agreed to that, Osberne raised his hand and told Hans to stand up, which the gunner did. Then he signed to Hans to follow him and Nato, so the gunner bade his four companions farewell, thinking that he must go to his death. Nevertheless, he walked with a firm step as a brave man should, going between Osberne and Nato, who said no word until they came to a flat place with many bushes, where they could be neither heard nor seen, and there Osberne and Nato stopped.

" Hans," said Osberne. " Do you know me? "

For the shortest moment the gunner stared, then he cried, "As I am a sinful man, it is Osberne. And we thought you dead. Oh, my boy! My boy! How glad I am to see you."

With that he ran forward and put his arms about Osberne, and the two stood, clapping each other on the back. Then they were confused, not knowing what to do or to say next, until there came forth a burst of questions, Osberne wanting to know about the ship, and Hans about what the lad had seen and done, and how he came to be there with the Indians. So an hour went as if on wings.

"And now for the plan," said Osberne, when they had made clear the first of things. "I have sworn to release Kenu and Cama and —"

"Ho! Ho!" said Hans. "Then you and your friends were on the *Concepcion* and did that trick at the time of the storm. Andrew told me he thought you had to do with it. And there was the writing man, Pigafetta, setting down about giants and conjurers and one thing and another."

"To shorten a long story, Hans, whoever is on the *San Antonio*, be he Kenu or Cama —"

"It is Cama, Osberne, and he is a very sick man."

"Then Cama I shall take from the ship and somehow set free," said Osberne.

"But your plan?"

"That you shall go on board, and I shall take you there with Nato helping me. Then you must say, as envoy, that if they set Cama free, the four seamen shall be delivered safely to the ship. The exchange can be made on the beach. What think you? The words of the ship men cannot be trusted."

"That is true, Osberne. But now it is different. There is trouble on the ship, and fast brewing too. Gomez and

Guerra are plotting to take the ship from Mesquita and sail back to Spain, and these men held by the Indians are all for the two Spaniards. Be sure that both Gomez and Guerra will be glad to treat for the men. But Gomez and Guerra think to find a way home without going through the strait again, for they fear to be stopped by Magellan. That is why we sail this way."

Then Osberne turned to Nato. "Is there a way to San Julian down this strait?" he asked.

"No," Nato answered. "It is a water with a mountain at the end," and Osberne told Hans what the Indian said.

"Then all the better," said Hans. "We shall have this man to tell them."

"Now, no word to the Spaniards that I am not what I seem to be," Osberne warned.

"And I? What is to become of me?" asked Hans.

"You shall come with us and a way will be found to put you with the fleet," answered Osberne.

"But you, lad?"

"Does a man leave friends trusted and true who love him, and he loves them in return, does he leave them willingly? No. I am for staying with them now and forever," answered Osberne.

"Lad, thou hast the gift of friendship," said Hans.

But all did not fall out as they planned. That night the five seamen sat about the fire, not so miserable as before because Hans told them of the plan to change them for the Indian held captive on the *San Antonio,* but he kept it a dark secret in his heart that Osberne lived with the Indians. In the morning the five sailors went down to the water's edge and stood there in full sight of the ship, so that those on board could see that they lived and were unhurt. But on board no move was made to offer fight, perhaps because of the strength of the Indians. Also messages had been sent in the night so that many canoe Indians had gathered about the bay, so the Indians far outnumbered the men on the *San Antonio,* ten to one and more. Another happy thing was that the ship lay so close to the shore, and the air was so still, that the sailors could shout to those on board and make themselves understood. So when Gomez the pilot called across the water, saying a word and stopping before he said the next word, what he said was clear. And Pedro de Valpuesta, a servant, one of the five on shore, called back that two Indians and Hans would come on board if safe conduct was promised.

"We want our men, not Indians," shouted back Gomez. "But the Indian will not be let go until the men are here."

"Let us go and talk sense to them," said Osberne to Nato. "And we shall make it clear to them that the way they would sail will lead to nowhere but shipwreck if the wind should be bad."

Thereupon Osberne and Nato and Hans went in a canoe and soon were aboard, nor did any men there guess Osberne to be other than an Indian, for Hans was careful to give no sign to the contrary. And soon it was settled that they would take Cama on a canoe halfway, the four men in the ship's boat being let go free and meeting the canoe where all would shake hands and so the exchange be made. Hans did the talking to Gomez, and both Osberne and Nato stood silent.

But while they talked, up came Guerra with some men-at-arms, and up came from another direction Mesquita the Captain, though he stood apart with his arms folded, looking on with a frown.

"And now," went on Hans, "I have learned one thing, and it is that the way we are to sail leads to a place where is no outlet and if we go that way we court danger with a contrary wind. This Indian called Nato is a pilot among his own people, and the other with him who stands here is his friend and blood brother. The pilot has skill to make a map of the waters."

Then Nato, at a sign from Hans, took a piece of red clay and drew lines showing the inlet, making it run south but with no opening so that a ship must turn round and come out by the way it went in; so Gomez and Guerra and Captain Mesquita began to argue, not gently but with heat.

"Our way is to the flagship which we are to meet in the straits somewhere to the west," shouted the captain, red with anger, though the cause of that anger neither Nato nor Osberne understood.

"And I say that our way is to Spain," shouted Guerra. "My kinsman, Cristobal de Haro who paid out good money for these ships has a say in this matter. We have found the strait and that is what we were sent out to do."

"Am I captain?" said Mesquita. He drew near Guerra and glared at him, and both men laid hands on their daggers.

"Gently, gently," said Gomez. "This will get us nothing. The matter of the four men is to be settled."

"Let the four men stay where they are, to die," said Mesquita. "I know them to be false traitors planning to mutiny."

"They are four good men and true," roared Guerra, almost choking with rage. "Let the Indian go, men." He said that because two sailors had brought Cama up from below, but the man was like a ghost, weak and famished and sick almost to

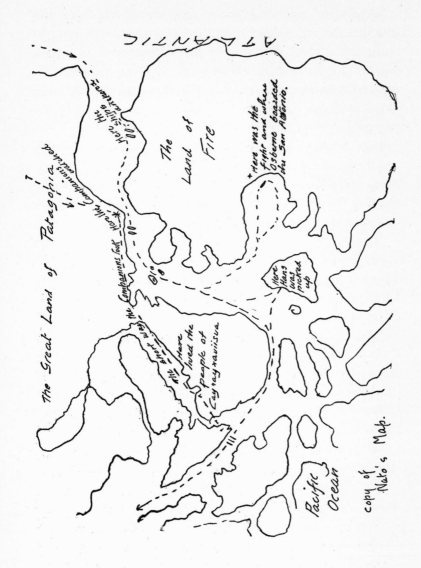

death, being so long in the dark hold with rats and vermin, and in stinking air.

"Put him in the canoe with these two dogs of Indians," ordered Guerra. "And send this fellow Hans with them. He is not with us but has always stood with Magellan the thief and tyrant; Magellan who sold his country to the Moors, as all men know. Let the Indians kill and eat the fellow."

"You lie!" shouted Mesquita, and ran at Guerra with uplifted dagger, but Gomez took a lance and pricked the captain in the breast, stopping him. At the same moment Guerra leaped like a lion and planted his dagger twice in Mesquita's side, and the captain gave a groan and fell to the deck bleeding freely.

"Chain him and take him to the hold where the Indian was," said Guerra, suddenly calm, wiping his dagger on his sleeve, whereupon three sailors carried the wounded man away.

But the men were strangely quiet, none offering to make trouble, or even to take part.

"I have challenged the captain many's the time, and now I lay aside my quarrel," Guerra said aloud, for all to hear. "If there is any man not content with what I have done, let him step forward."

Then Gomez stood up and raised his sword. "Hear me! Geronimo Guerra has put his noble person in jeopardy to do what is right and proper," he said. "The greater part of the cost of this fleet has been borne by that rich merchant, Cristobal de Haro, a kinsman to Guerra. And now the strait we were sent out to find has been found, wherefore I say it is right and proper to return to Spain. Magellan, it is whispered, goes to deliver the fleet to the Portuguese traitor Serrao. So, seeing what should be done, I proclaim Geronimo Guerra captain of this ship, the *San Antonio*. If there be any man not with us, let him step forward."

" I am not with you," called out Hans, stepping forward. " Right or wrong, the duty is to the admiral. The straight road and the shortest to the flagship should be this captain's first order if he is any true captain."

Guerra fell into a muse, or seemed to, for he said nothing for a while. Then he stood up, a man with eyes of steel set in a brown face, a man hardy and keen and bright, tall and straight, so that all there thought him a proper captain.

" My first order is this," he said. " The straight and the shortest road for the disobedient is hanging at the end of a rope, and that road I am minded that you, Hans, should take. But I will be merciful, doing as Magellan did to our friend and companion Juan de Cartagena. You shall go ashore with this Indian prisoner and the two with him. So we shall do well by the savages, giving them four men for our four men."

" May the saints help him with those eaters of men's bodies," said one sailor, for the ship men held the natives to be cannibals.

" Not a word more," said Guerra, shaking his finger at the speaker, and went to the waist of the ship.

So Hans and Osberne and Cama and Nato were put into the canoe and they paddled away, all of them grinning and pleased. At the same time the Indians on shore, being guided by Ato, pushed off the boat with the four seamen. Then the two boats met midway and all shook hands as had been agreed upon.

But when Osberne and Pedro de Valpuesta shook hands, and when Pedro had rubbed the palms of his hands together, think-ing himself somehow soiled because of touching an Indian as he supposed Osberne to be, great was his surprise to hear the Indian say, in a whisper, "Tell your shipmates and Juan de Cartagena that the lad from Portsdown with his friends has stolen back two kidnapped men. Of the third you may never hear, but he too shall go free, though I have to lay down my life in the freeing of him."

At noon they saw the *San Antonio* stand out to sea under a fair wind, and knew that she had deserted the fleet, and that Magellan with three ships was left to do the best that he could. But with the *San Antonio* went the most of the stores, and the war things, and some good men too.

CHAPTER IX

The Freeing of Kenu

GOOD-BYE to the *San Antonio*," said Hans. "Her
captain has deserted and the loss of the ship leaves
the fleet poor indeed. The greater part of the stores
are in the hold. The best part of the arms too."

"And many good men," added Osberne.

"Now it is easy to see what your chief will do," said Nato to
Osberne. "Tired of waiting he will send a ship back. But
your chief will wait where his ship lies and where our companions watch it. The ship he sends will not come this way but the
same way she went, and we, watching from the island of seals,
will see it."

"So on that island we can put Hans that he may be picked
up," said Osberne.

"That pleases me," said Hans, "but I find it in my heart, Osberne, to wish that you went with me."

"Not so," answered Osberne. "I sleep sweetly in this land and with these people. They are a mighty folk, and while I can teach them a few things, they can teach me much more. I like the cleanness of the land too. Also it is my task to rescue the boy Kenu before he sickens, as Cama has sickened. Then I shall fare forth and see all this land, with my companions. I shall go to the La Plata river. I shall see new things and meet new people. Give my love to Andrew and tell him that we may meet some day, and if you reach Portsdown, then see Sir Robert and give him a letter that I shall write and get to you or to Andrew. If I make no mistake, he will come to this land with his good ship *Seagull*, not killing and plundering as these do in their greed for gold, but coming in friendship. That is my plan."

"Friend and fellow, I like the spirit of it," said Hans, "but have no fear, never a word shall I say on the ship, except to Andrew. It is in his mind, as it is in my mind, to go round the world. Then knowing the way, and knowing these straits, we shall tell the story to other brave captains. Sir Robert is a likely man to try the venture. With him it would be very glorious."

Osberne told all that to Ato and his friends, after which all of them said a farewell to the Ona Indians, and there were words of good-will. Then, as was the custom, the chief of the Onas gave each one a bow and arrow of best make and all went down to the seashore. So the canoes with Osberne and his friends, with Hans, pushed off into a sea on which there was hardly a ripple. A little way out, and away from the shelter of the land, they caught a light breeze, so went merrily until they came to the island that Nato had told them of. They pulled the canoes on shore and walked inland, over the shoulder of a mountain and across a lower ridge, and so came in sight of the channel through which any ship searching for the *San Antonio* must pass. It was the same channel at the upper end of which lay Magellan's flagship. They had a meal, then found a place by the sea for Hans, so that he had shelter and warmth and food, though they stayed with him until the ship that sought the runaway *San Antonio* hove in sight, when Osberne and the others hid. But they did not go far, nor was it needful to do so, for well they knew that the ship men feared to go on land. Indeed they were so near, and the air was so clear that they could hear the noises of the ship when the *Victoria* came abreast of the point where Hans stood. They heard the talk of the men, and the creaking of the ropes and blocks, and the flapping and snapping of the flag at the mast-head, and the hour-glass boy as he called out the time and struck the bell.

There was Hans lamely running along the beach and waving his cap and hailing the ship as if in sore distress and fear; and there on board, as Osberne and the rest saw, were the men all crowded to the side to see what was to be seen, and Andrew among them.

"A good time indeed will Hans and Andrew have telling and hearing all this," said Osberne to Ato and Nato.

"Now look what a game Hans plays," said Nato. "He goes down to the edge of the water as if his legs had been broken, and his back wrenched, and his eyes half blinded."

"You would say that he had eaten nothing for a month," said Nato, "so weak he seems. Yet six good fish he managed only an hour ago."

Then they heard the pilot cry across the strip of water, " Ho! Are there savages about? "

" I have been among them but escaped," called Hans, making a speaking trumpet of his hands.

So the ship hove to and a boat was lowered, but while that was being done the talk went on.

" Where is the *San Antonio?* " shouted the pilot.

" Deserted and gone to Spain," answered Hans.

" But what do you here? "

" They put me ashore because I would not stand for Guerra and Gomez," answered Hans, then told the men to haste and acted in the manner of one greatly worried and in much fear. " Haste! " he said again and again. And when the men were rowing to the shore, he called, " Make no noise for the Indians have ears that hear many miles, and eyes that see ten times the distance their ears hear." And he hobbled a little way along the beach to a place from which his shelter could not be seen, shouting, " This is the place to land."

So the boat scraped the shore, and Osberne and his friends saw Hans step into it; saw the men push off with their oars against the rocks; saw the boat return to the ship. They saw the men climb on board, and then lost sight of Hans because the seamen crowded round. Next the helmsman put the ship in the light wind, and the sails cracked and filled, and the *Victoria* sailed round the point and out of sight, in hot chase of the *San Antonio.* But that ship they never found, for by the time the *Victoria* reached the opening of the strait the *San Antonio* was far out to sea headed for Spain.

Rolda-aka and Baka, watching on the headland, saw the *San Antonio* hurrying eastward under a fair wind. They saw also the *Victoria* looking for her, but the men on one ship could not see the other ship. They watched the *Victoria* go to the mouth of the strait then turn back, so they knew that their watching on the headland had come to an end. Off then they went, following the trail that Osberne and the others had taken, straight across the shining country to the place where the fishers lived on the inland sea. And across that sea they sped, using a sail as Osberne had taught them, and presently came to the place where Mako and Nio the quick-sighted, and Tenka the strong watched, living with the people of Cayrayxaviisus. A low ridge hid them from the two ships that lay anchored in the mouth of the river of many fish, but over that ridge the seamen never went, fearing so much to go inland. But the Patagonians looked down from the ridge top on to the ships and saw all that was to be seen. So close under the ridge lay the ship that had the Patagonians been so minded, they could have shot arrows and picked the seamen off one at a time. Indeed once Tenka played a trick when he saw a man, which chanced to be Espinosa, beating a ship boy. For Tenka took his sling, put a stone in it and shot so that the missile took Espinosa on the chest. The bully dropped the boy and stood up, grunting and cursing and looking about the ship for the one who had thrown the stone, never guessing that it came from the ridge. Thereafter, for the rest of that morning Tenka watched, and every now and then let loose a stone, taking Espinosa in the back, or on the head, or on the arm, until the constable of the fleet began to believe the place bewitched, and ran below, shouting.

It was well past the middle of the night when the canoe with Osberne and Ato and Nato came, not landing near the ships but in a haven close by; then they carried their canoes across the land to the Indian encampment. So all the companions were together again and a merry time they made of it, the merrier because the man Cama, in that clean air, with plenty of good food, seemed somewhat to have gotten better of his sickness, though he was still weak.

But something happened on the morning of the next day when Tenka and Osberne and Nio watched from the crest of the ridge. For they saw their Indian companion, the boy Kenu, brought up on to the deck chained hand and foot. A man-at-arms and the writing man Pigafetta were with him.

"They ask him questions as they always do," said Nio. "The man with the book writes down what he says."

"And how looks the boy Kenu?" asked Osberne.

"Weary, most weary," answered Nio.

"I am for running down and swimming to the ship, fighting a way to the boy," said Tenka.

"You would be stuck full of arrows like a porcupine," said Nio. "There are archers, and men with guns everywhere. They get ready to sail I think."

"No. This cannot be done by force," said Osberne. "We must trick them some way."

"The boy Kenu knows that we are near," said Nio. "He cannot keep his eyes from the ridge, though they point out this and that, wishing him to look at things. The writing man now and then touches a man-at-arms and asks some question I think."

"What the writing man tries to do is to get the Indian names of things," said Osberne.

"But Kenu will not look at the things," said Nio. "His eyes are fixed this way. It may be that he sees us. I think he does."

"His heart is with his friends," said Tenka. "And his heart

shall be made glad," added the giant. Thereupon he stood up, in full sight of the ship, to be seen by all men against the sky, and waved his cloak to the boy. "What care I for what these fools think," said Tenka. "I am for my friend though they kill me."

The others pulled him down, but it was too late. Those on the ship had seen the Patagonians, and, seeing, were full of strange fear. On the two ships men were pointing to the ridge. They called and others came running up from below. The friends on the ridge somehow knew the anger and fear in the ships. They could see one man standing somewhat apart, waving his arms and pointing, and Osberne thought that he persuaded the others to make an onslaught. All that day the seamen and the men-at-arms worked, getting cannon up on deck, preparing lances and crossbows. They stuck javelins around the mast, and many of the men put on breastplates. Then, to strike terror into the hearts of the Indians, they fired bombards again and again so that the noise echoed from the mountains, twice, and thrice, as though cannon had been planted in the rooted hills. Also thereafter, guards were set who walked up and down the deck all day, and at night braziers were lighted and men with lanterns went up and down. But no man went ashore from the ships and the boats were not lowered. And thus things stood until the *Victoria* came from her quest and anchored beside the other two ships. That ship too armed herself.

Only there was this. On the ridge top some of the companions always watched, day and night, two by two. One morning, early, when Ato and Nio were on guard, they saw a man on the nearest ship whom they knew to be Andrew, by the white kerchief he always wore. He seemed to be on guard, and the other with him they knew to be Hans, because no man on the ships was square-built as he.

" I shall show myself," said Ato. " There can be no harm in it for these two are our friends and it may be that they shall make some sign that we can understand." .

So Ato stood up, and Nio too stood and faced him, then the two made the sign of friendship one with the other, knowing that against the sky as they stood those on the ship could see them.

" One of them makes ready to shoot," said Nio.

It was Andrew. They saw him prepare his crossbow and sight it, then let fly his bolt, but they marked where it fell, and as it curved to its fall Nio of the sharp eye caught the flash of something white. So Nio threw himself flat on the ground and began to wriggle from bush to bush like a snake, and at last came to the place where the bolt fell, and found it. And there, tied to the bolt he found a rag of parchment with markings on it. But on the ships there were men with quick eyes who made out the figure to be an Indian, so they set up a great shouting, and some began to shoot their crossbows, but to no effect. Nio hid himself well, keeping behind bushes and grass tufts, and gained the ridge top. Then he ran down to the camp and woke Osberne. And this is what Osberne read.

We sail this midnight. Make no attack for fear of great bloodshed. Kenu is here chained and sick. Would I could loose him to you. Farewell. Andrew.

Not one word spoke any of the Indians when Osberne told them what it was all about. Osberne was the first to break the silence.

" There is only one way," he said. " I shall go on the ship

as soon as it is dark and somehow free the lad. He must not suffer so. To sail on the sea would be his death."

Then uprose Macho the quiet. "I should go," he said. "I can slip about quiet as a mouse, and as quick."

"I should go with you to break the chains," said Tenka the strong.

"Not so. It will not do," Osberne said. "You will go with me to the beach, both of you. There will be work enough to do. Nio too must go to see what we cannot see. Ato will be there with us. Baka as well, for he may have to run to bring help. But I alone shall go to the ship. I shall return with Kenu. Or if I do not return, then Kenu shall come and you shall see me again, if not soon, then at a later time."

"It will not do. We cannot leave you," said Rolda-aka. "At least let me swim with you to the ship for company's sake."

"You may do that and hang in the chains until Kenu comes. Then swim back with him. But do not climb up into the ship or you must be a dead man." Osberne spoke with great seriousness and Rolda-aka nodded his head as a child might do.

"It makes my heart sad to hear you say that you might not come back," said Ato.

"Ato, my friend and brother, it is my will to come back to you," said Osberne. "My heart is with all of you. I love you as true men. With you I have seen dawn and seen sunset. With you I have seen the stars smile. We have known many good days. So I would not leave you. But if I come not back, then know that it is because I cannot. But spill no blood trying to save me. Promise me that."

They promised most heartily.

"I shall be trying always to come back, if they hold me there," Osberne went on. "But if it comes to pass that they take me away, though I do not believe that they will, then before many suns I shall come again in a new ship, and with men not of a mind to spill blood."

So when night came Osberne and his companions went down to the edge of the sea and saw the lanterns glimmering on the ships, and the shadows of men going up and down on the deck. Osberne went into the water up to his waist, his companions going with him, and there they touched one another's shoulders in farewell, but spoke no word. Already the water began to run swift with the tide, so there was no time to lose. The last to whom Osberne spoke was Ato, and he saw the Indian's eyes glittering like two stars.

" Ma-ee-ya, Ato," he whispered.

" Ma-ee-ya, Ota-bben," whispered Ato in return.

Osberne and Rolda-aka swam, going with the current and making no more sound than an otter. Under a bed of kelp they had to dive, because of the long tangling stems. They came to the ship's side and both wondered a little seeing it stand so high and black, but they kept off somewhat and found the chains and there rested awhile. And, while they hung there, a yellow light came all about them when a man with a lantern looked over the side. But the two swimmers knew that he could not see beyond the light he held, so they kept quiet. When the man went away Osberne climbed up the chain and so came to a place where he could raise his head and look along the deck, much as he had done at San Julian, but he dropped back into the darkness, for so close that he could have touched him by stretching forth his hand stood a man-at-arms with a lantern at his feet. And about the deck lay other men asleep, with lances by them. Had the guard been turned the other way he must have seen Osberne without a doubt. After a while Osberne heard the man's tread as he walked down the deck, then again he raised his head. This time none were there but sleeping men. Also he thought fortune with him, because he saw himself to be in a wedge of darkness made by the mast, for on the other side of the mast a lantern stood on the deck. So Osberne, swift and quiet as a cat, slipped by way of the bowsprit's foot to the deck. But no sooner had he done so than the wedge of dark moved, and from behind the mast came a guard, with pike and lantern, yawning greatly but looking about him. With a quick move Osberne stepped into the shadow which by that time had swung to the larboard side, though he had to hop over a sleeper to do so. Then a mad thought came to Osberne and saved him. He ran up the bowsprit to where the stay that held the mainmast was fastened, then swarmed up the stay to the dark below the lookout, because a man with a lantern was there, watching. Thus he could look down on the deck and see the open hold, and the men sleeping and on watch, and the lanterned castle aft of the ship, and the sails partly unloosed so as to be ready to lift when the tide served. He also noted that some men were making ready to sail, and the mate went about grumbling and cursing; also at the fore end of the ship there were men busying themselves at the anchor and getting ropes ready.

For a little time Osberne hung on in torture of mind and body. It made his heart heavy as a stone to think of being so near the prisoned Kenu yet unable to get to him because of men on deck and about the hold opening, and with so short a time left before the ships must sail. And never had man more cause to dread when he heard the mate tell the men to rouse themselves and get to the tops to make ready the topsails. Had he as much as a coat, he would have tried mingling boldly with the men on deck, keeping in the shadows, but bare to the waist as he was, to move was to be known as an enemy and Indian. So he hung for a time that seemed unending, the ropes bruising his legs. Then the deck grew bright with torches as men gathered at the foot of the mast, and in the light he saw sleepers waking and rousing themselves, and nothing seemed able to save him from destruction when some should swarm up the ratlines. At one moment he thought of diving into the sea, and would have done so had it not been for a new idea. For he saw one of the sleepers arise and throw off a coat he had used as a blanket, then thrust it between the ratlines, after which the man went forward. At the same instant the men with torches ran to the whipstaff because the mate called them, and he cursing most lustily because of something jammed tight, so all the waist of the ship was left in darkness. Down went Osberne, going by the ratlines, and in the pocket of the coat he found a woolen knitted cap such as all the sailors had, so he felt that it would be hard for anyone to know him in the hurly-burly and noise, dressed in the sailor's cap and coat. None the less he kept a sharp eye open.

" Now the saints bring me safe through this! " he said, as he dropped into the dark hold, nor did he take ten steps before he had to stop and wipe the sweat from his forehead, so close and stinking was the air. He found the prison cell and began fumbling with the bolts in the dark, his ears pricked for the sound of footsteps. And in spite of the danger, he felt the pang of hunger, for with the excitement he had not eaten much that day, and the swim and the waiting had sharpened his appetite. But everything went well, and he swung the door open and found Kenu in chains. The lad gave a low cry of joy seeing Osberne, for he knew him before Osberne could as much as make out the form of the Indian, the prisoner having lain so long in utter darkness.

"But how to loose you?" said Osberne, much puzzled. "Were Tenka here he would make short work of the chains."

Then Kenu begged Osberne to go and leave him. "The man called Espinosa keeps the key," he told Osberne, and showed a lock that held the chain to a great staple. "Better it would be that you found a knife and took my life. See, I bare my breast for the stroke."

"Then Espinosa I shall find," said Osberne. "Fear not. This night you shall see your companions."

"I am too weak to swim," said Kenu.

"Rolda-aka waits in the chains and he will help you," Osberne replied. Then he said, whispering, "I shall shut the door and seek out Espinosa. If not, then I shall stay with you, and find a way to free you. But then I must go and tell Rolda-aka, who waits."

With that Osberne turned away and softly closed the door, then climbed again to the deck. But he kept to the shadows, always going in the manner of one in a hurry to do an errand, so that those against whom he knocked, and they were many, never suspected him of being other than a shipmate. And there were men coming and going, and others shouting, all of whom he knew, but no sight did he get of either Andrew or Hans. By great good fortune, in a cabin in the after part of the ship he saw a door open, and, looking as he passed, beheld the writing man, Pigafetta, at work on his book. So he slipped into the cabin, closed the door after him, and took a sword from the wall. At the sound Pigafetta looked up, not alarmed, for he was a man of cool head.

"Take not a musket to kill a fly," said Pigafetta, smiling in a way that made Osberne feel foolish.

"I intend you no harm," said Osberne. "Rely on me to return this."

"I am the only one of my friends I can rely on," answered Pigafetta. "But why this adventure? I know you for the English lad."

"There is no time," said Osberne. "I am to rescue the boy Kenu and —"

"Enough," said Pigafetta, rising from his seat. "The lad is in my charge and I am making a book of words from him. You would take away my study."

Then Osberne flashed into a sudden rage. "You keep a man captive for your silly books! If it is only that, let him go and I shall stay, who know the Indian tongue."

"Tut! Tut!" said Pigafetta. "I am more than partly with you. Now let us do first and talk after. Here is the key. Get your friend away and keep a silent tongue. Go and lose no time."

Never was Osberne more amazed. He tried to say thanks but stammered.

"Go," said Pigafetta, and pushed him to the door gently. "I have no wish to keep these poor folk in this misery."

Then Osberne ran to the prison cell, not keeping to shadows this time but making straight for the hold. Much was he cursed by those he ran against as a fool and a clumsy lout, but never had man more joyful heart. While he unlocked the chain he heard a trumpet sound, and knew it for the sailing order. But the lock was hard to undo and he cast off his coat and cap the better to work, for haste called. Then having opened the lock, he picked up Kenu and carried him on his

Kanu Escapes

shoulders, though the lad was near being a man in stature, and heavy enough. Up on deck he thrust him, then himself followed. Again he hoisted him on his back and thus laden ran down the deck, going to the chains forward. One man he knocked against went sprawling on the deck. Another, seeing him coming, stood aside and lifted his lantern. Then having seen he raised his voice and called out, "Indians! To arms! Indians!" Others took up the cry. Men at work with the sails stopped to see, and some ran forward. A man-at-arms ran at Osberne, sword in hand and buckler raised. Another stood in front, boldly enough, crying, "No passage!" and opened his arms to stop the runaway. But Osberne met him in full shock and he went down. Osberne ran into other men, some of whom smote where they could, striking him on the head and in the face with fists and sticks or sticking him with lances. Often he escaped by leaping aside nimbly. Often he was hurt. One, a great man and tall, threw himself down in Osberne's path so that the lad stumbled and almost fell, but chanced to bring up against the bulwark close to the anchor chain. Furiously then he strove to get Kenu over the side, for many hands hampered him. Twice he called down to Rolda-aka, bidding him stay where he was and watch, and most happy he felt to hear the answering voice of the Indian below. Then Kenu half fell, half leaped overboard, so Osberne knew that part of his task to be done and knew that the lad would return to his companions. True he was chained and hampered, but the strong swimmer Rolda-aka would be with him. But when Osberne tried to climb, in spite of the hands clutching at him, he felt a pain like a red-hot iron run through his leg, so knew that he had been stabbed. And a snarling voice made him turn, so that he saw the fox-face and black chin of Espinosa.

"Spy and traitor!" shouted Espinosa as he thrust at him with a sword the blade of which went through the flesh of his arm.

"Ma-ee-ya!" called out Osberne, and two voices from the sea shouted back, "Ma-ee-ya! Ota-bben!"

Once more Osberne strove, catching with his hands in spite of his wound at the ratlines and lifting himself from the deck. But a noose was thrown over his head and it fell about his throat, choking him when it was pulled tight. So he fell back, nearly strangled. Then others bound him hand and foot, and afterwards dragged him with many blows and curses and kicks to the foot of the mainmast. Others picked him up and dropped him into the black hold, but it all seemed like a dream. And so he lay prisoner, faint and bleeding, while the ships sailed away.

CHAPTER X

The Crossing of the Pacific

I AM WOUNDED most grievously," said Osberne, as he
lay in his blood, looking up through the opening of the
hold through which he could see the stars swinging from
side to side as the ship rolled. "It is strange how little I feel
pain with it all," he thought, and with the thought he seemed
to fall into a deep and black pit. Then he fancied himself to
be resting by a quiet stream, lying in coolest grass, with Ato
and others of his companions sitting near, so that his heart
leaped with joy that the misery on the ship was only a bad
dream. He began to ask questions about the fleet and thought
he heard Ato say, "Forbear thy questions now and let me do
this." Then Ato changed into rough-bearded Andrew who

was putting cool bandages on Osberne's wounds and holding a cup of water to his lips. So a sickness came over the lad and he could hardly forbear sobbing.

"I am hard and clumsy I know," said Andrew. "Bear with me the best you can."

Osberne wanted to say something of thanks, but could only wearily shake his head. Words would not come.

Another time he came out of darkness thinking himself to be with the Indians, and with Patagonian children all happy and bright-eyed, watching them pluck great handfuls of flowers and listening to their song. So he felt very happy in the glowing world. But the sky closed down on him and turned black, and the air grew most foul and close, and the earth changed from softness to great hardness, and his friends who had been all laughter and smiles seemed to look on him coldly and to talk of stone walls of separation. That saddened him because he had found friendship to be clean understanding and frankness, therefore he wept a little, and stretched out his hands for his friends, calling on them to return. He opened his eyes to see the fox-faced, black-chinned Espinosa looking down at him.

Once he woke to find himself talking, saying something long since forgotten which he had heard a man in Portsdown read out of a book. And it was this: *They have stricken me . . . they have beaten me and I felt it not. When shall I awake? I will seek it yet again.* He searched his memory for more but found nothing except, *Thou leadest me beside still waters.* So he said that aloud, knowing that some one heard, and that some one being Nato of the brown eye. He went on, "It is a long night, and we must be nearing the open sea, Nato."

"Hearken, lad," answered the one he had thought to be

Nato. "Hearken lad! Be of good heart and rouse yourself. This is Hans, your friend, and it wrings my heart to see you thus. Know me, dear lad, for what I am."

"I know you, Hans," answered Osberne, and tried to lift himself in his bed, but fell back wearily. Nor could he bring himself to say more.

"Know the truth, lad. It may help," said Hans. "Not one night but fourteen have passed, and we are far out at sea. But it grieves me to hear you talk of your lost friends, and how others have stricken and beaten you. And you are awake. Lad, you have been near death, but now you shall live again and be strong. There shall come many a fair day for us all."

But that Osberne could not understand in his weakness. So he turned his face away from Hans and slept again. After that he slipped into darkness for many days.

He awoke to find himself in a clean cabin with a window that gave on the deep blue ocean, and white running waves. But the sky was hard blue, and the sun golden and fierce and hot, wherefore Osberne found none of the joy of looking at the sea that he had known at Portsdown. So he turned himself the other way, though with much pain and effort, and beheld a man with eyes gray and steady. He did not see more than the eyes because of a mist, and because it wearied him to look away from the eyes, but he knew the man to be Pigafetta.

"Well enough," said Pigafetta. "Now you shall mend and do well again. Life lieth before you now."

"I must get up," said Osberne, and in his mind he meant to do that but because of his sorry weakness found himself unable to make a move other than to turn his head.

"Yes," said Pigafetta merrily, but softly. "You must get up. And you must make a hole in the water. And you must carry water in a sieve. And you must dry the sea with a sponge. And you must teach fish to swim. And you must sew your coat with a red-hot needle and a burnt thread. You must do all of those and more, if you can. Then you must dig a well with a needle, and look for fire under ice, and take a spear to kill a fly, and make a rope of sand, and catch the wind with a net. So rest awhile until you are ready."

"But . . . I . . . have lain . . . too long," said Osberne, and as he spoke he wondered at the way his words came, with long spaces between them.

"Long is not forever," answered Pigafetta. "Had you not lain so long then you would have lain forever, lad."

That was the moment of Osberne's mending, though for many days he could not get to the deck but must needs stay in the cabin, taking what water, boiled and cooled, that Andrew and Hans brought to him, but eating very little except a flying fish that had chanced to fall on the deck, and which one of his friends prepared and cooked. But Pigafetta would have kept him in his cabin still longer, for whenever he could get Osberne in the mind, he would have him telling him Patagonian words, which he wrote down. What seemed most strange to Osberne was that he never saw his friends Hans and Andrew in the day time, but always at dark. Another strange thing was that none of those who came to the cabin told about the journey and how it prospered.

"You do not tell me the day," said Osberne, the morning before he went on deck for the first time. "Nor do I know what places we have seen. Surely we have not been on a landless sea."

"We sailed for two months west," said Pigafetta, "before we came to an island, but on it were no people and no animals, nor could we find anchorage. Eleven days later we came to another island, but with no water nor fruit nor people, only birds and trees, and the fish called tiburoni. We named it the Desaventurada because of bad luck. We left there on the fourth day of February, which was three days ago."

Osberne lay awhile scarce moving, trying to picture what he had been told, and trying to understand the great length of time that had passed.

"It was in November that I last saw my friends, the Indians," he said.

"The last day of November," answered Pigafetta. "I marked it in my book, ' We passed the longed-for cape on the twenty-eighth day of November of the year fifteen hundred and twenty, and named it therefore Cape Deseado.' So runs the passage. We have been on this sea now for sixty and nine days and no sight of land."

"But what speed do we make?" asked Osberne.

"By the measure of the chain at the poop we run sixty or seventy leagues each day. It is a sea so vast that the mind of man can hardly grasp it," answered Pigafetta a little sadly. Then he cheered up somewhat and said, "But he that will have no trouble in this world must not be born in it."

"It is well that the water and food hold out," said Osberne, at which Pigafetta smiled in a sad way.

"You have been lucky wanting so little food," said Pigafetta after a while. "A sick man has small interest in the kitchen."

Osberne did not understand that until some days later when he climbed to the deck, wondering much at the weakness of his legs, going very painfully. He did not know his shipmates, so much like ghosts they seemed. They were bearded and gaunt; and their rags hung upon them like clothes on sticks; and their eyes looked out of deep hollows; and their cheeks had fallen in; and so weak they were that four men could not pull on a rope with the strength of one hale man. They spoke seldom, but when they did their voices came rough and rasping. When the boy with water came, and it was the slave Enrique, the thirst-ridden men held their noses as they drank, because of the stench of the foul draught, nor was any man given more than a mouthful. But the most of the men chose to mix the drink with a sort of powder, and that powder the ship's biscuit that had fallen into crumbs, and those full of worms, and stinking because of rats. Two men he saw had caught a rat and skinned it, and when they had boiled it they drank the soup and picked the bones clean.

"Tell me, Enrique, by what kindness of some one did I have water while I lay sick," asked Osberne when he found the slave in a quiet place one day. "Was it the admiral? Once he showed some good-will to me at San Julian."

"It was Andrew and Hans," replied Enrique. "They took only half of their water, setting aside the rest for you and boiling it. When you would not drink, crying out upon them for offering you foul water, as you often did in your madness, then one of them knelt down by you and held your head and the other put the cup to your lips. So it went, in the dark hold, until the chevalier Pigafetta saw. Then he had them carry you to his cabin and tended you."

"And I, all the while, mourning for those other friends and not knowing what these did for me," said Osberne. "But I cannot see them to thank them. Where are they?"

"They were sent on the *Victoria* and are there now, but I have heard that Andrew lies sick and helpless."

Then Enrique went away and Osberne sat there alone in the shadow of the sail, which was black and torn. And there he often rested, gathering strength day after day, but with a brain pained and wearied. For the world was a world of blue water, and the sky a sky of beryl blue, and the sun a fire-ball that went its course baking the ships and searing the men. No sign of life, no joy, no noise of calling birds were there. Did a man move but a few yards, then he must needs stand gasping, with swollen tongue and tightened throat. A cloud in the sky would have been welcome as an angel, but no cloud came. A storm would have come as the gift of God, but no storm came, only the slow and steady wind which moved the ships, but that came burning hot, bringing anguish.

So wore the days sadly. The three ships were castles of grief, too sad to hail, too sad to wave greeting when they sighted one another after the haze of dawn vanished. There was no joy and no hope, because there were no busy hours. Men passed and repassed not looking at one another, all of them wearied and frightened and anxious. Their bodies lived but their brains were dead. There were some who stood for hours gazing into the sea. Others lay in one place, hardly rousing themselves to take the stinking water. But worst of all were those who wept sorely as they went about their tasks. And many lay sick of the scurvy, their arms and legs swollen and their mouths bleeding and their teeth falling out. In seven days seven of them died and were thrown overboard, without tear or prayer.

Then, when they had sailed for ninety and eight days after leaving the straits, and on a morning when Enrique and Osberne stood together, Pigafetta came up and said, " Lads, what seest thou? Is it a cloud or is it land?"

"Land it is," answered the slave. "I know it by the feel in me more than by the sight."

"Then say nothing until we make certain," said Pigafetta. "It would not be well to raise false hopes."

"But it is certain," said Enrique. "And while it is not my own land, it is a land I have seen before. There are mountains there which I know by the shape. And there will be people there who sail in swift boats which we call praus. I have looked long and carefully and know the place."

"Now that opens up a strange thing," said Pigafetta, "for if you know this place, having seen it, and if you see it now a second time coming from another way, then you are the first man to have gone round the world. So take care! Take care! If it be so then hold your tongue about it, for all fame is dangerous. It would never do for the slave to be first and not the master."

"If I set my foot again among my own people I care nothing for the glory," said Enrique. "If it be fame and glory, then it all costs too much. But it is a mad way to get home, and by so many leagues of bad road. Nor do I understand how I get home by going away from it. But this I know, it is land that we see and nothing but land." Then he put his hands to his mouth and shouted, "I see land! I see land!"

So all on the ship were in strange mood with all the sadness gone. Men who had been near dead went with a shuffling run, crowding to the forecastle to be nearer to the land by the ship's length. The very air changed, for there came a sweet smell of trees and of herbs, and soon after the ships had let down their anchors a gentle cool breeze came through the gates of the evening. Good to see was the swift life of birds, and the green of a fair space of meadow land, and hills dark with trees, and slopes of woodland that came down to the edge of the water. Wonderful too were the light praus, a sort of double canoe joined with a platform, with a tri-sail of woven grass, and on the boats laughing men. So swift flew the strange craft that the sailors stood agape to see them. None of the natives had weapons of any sort, not as much as an arrow or a knife or a spear. But the boats were bright with flowers and with fruits of many colors, and those looked better to the men than gold or jewels. And the brown men laughed when the sailors took the fruit, and laughed again so that their white teeth showed to see how the starving men ate with eagerness; nor was payment asked or offered. A man or two, thinking to make return for kindness, put gifts of looking-glasses and trinkets on boards and set them afloat for the natives to pick up, which they did. Then when Magellan ordered the skiff to be lowered into the water, so that he might go ashore when minded, the natives thought the boat to be a gift or payment, as the trinkets on boards had been, and when they went ashore they took the skiff with them, but that was in the darkness that came swift on the heels of evening, nor was the loss of the skiff known until morning.

Then when the loss of the skiff became known there arose a mighty to-do. Magellan, the meekness of hunger gone, swore roundly that he would burn the houses and lay waste the land to get his stolen skiff back. Espinosa ranted that the islands should be called the land of robbers, and named them the Ladrones, instead of the Lateen-sail Islands as the admiral had named them. But of all that flurry Osberne knew nothing because he was with some who had been sent to the *Victoria* with a letter, and there he met Andrew and Hans, both of them like changed men, and Andrew so sick that he lay without stirring.

"He is sick unto death," Hans whispered, hearing which Osberne found himself as one stricken dumb with grief.

"And I live," Osberne said when he gained speech again, "because he starved himself of water, as did you, that I might drink."

"Say no more of that," whispered the sick man. "If it was a kindness, then let one kindness be the price of another."

He spoke so soft, because of his ebbing life, that Hans and Osberne had to bend and hold their breaths to hear.

"Is there a thing you would have us do, shipmate?" asked Hans.

After a long space they heard Andrew again, but his words came between gaspings for breath.

"Yes," he said. "Steal me away to land and lay me there. I'll go no further, alive or dead, with these who bring pain wherever they set foot. If I live I shall fear no evil among these people. And now I am done. May the good God pardon my iniquity for it is great."

He said no more after that.

"He is a true man and not afraid to die," said Hans. "Let us do as he asks."

So they went to Miguel Sanchez, the mate, a young man of some twenty odd years, and one full of high-hearted friendliness and good-will. He heard their story, and hearing, looked much troubled.

"A sturdy heart, the man Andrew," he said. "A fellow hardy and brave, but I have seen death on his face for many weeks. But hearken, both of you. The letter you brought

from the admiral bids me take ten of my good men and go
ashore to fight these people, meeting ten men from the *Trinidad* and others from the *Concepcion*. It is a shameful thing
all this blood-letting, but the ox must go to the yoke at the
call of his master, and both Magellan and Espinosa are masterful men and overbearing. So I give you an order to make all
fall out well. I shall send you ashore to look over the land;
and watch, if you bear it in mind, that no others of their
kindred come to help the Indians we are to fight. Once in a
while that has been done in battle, so they say. So you may
look to our Andrew, old and spent and worn as he is. I would
give him my poor prayers but I fear that I am too sinful a
man to be heard."

Then the mate turned and began to shout in a rough voice
for the seamen to hear, calling ten men by name and bidding
them take their arquebuses. He added, "And you, Osberne,
with Hans and Andrew and Enrique, will take the skiff and
go ashore to yon point, keeping out of sight of the savages.
And look well to it that you kill the sons of dogs if any come
to help those who have stolen the admiral's skiff. If you fail,
look for punishment. And now begone and no words. Men,
lower the skiff and get them off."

Thus it came about that the three men rowed to shore with
their sick companion and they handling him tenderly, and
when they were a bowshot from shore he revived somewhat,
making a sign that he would speak. So they lay on their
oars to hear.

"I would see once more," he said, "the ripples as they run
up on the sea sand, curling white, with the green water white-
laced. And worry not at all, lads. It is well with me this day.
Tell me how the land looks."

" There is a space of sea-sand between the sea and the trees," said Osberne.

" And the sea runs all gentle-like," added Hans.

" And it is a peaceful place," said Osberne.

" Well," whispered Andrew, very softly because of the weariness that grew on him, " it is said that if a man stay silent he shall have peace. So farewell! I shall say no more."

So they came to the shore and there lifted Andrew out and laid him as he had wished so that he could see the sea, then Osberne went to a spring and brought to Andrew a cup of cool water, but he did no more than put his lips to it. For a little while they looked at his brave face, weary and white, seeing him also as he had been, gray-eyed and kind of countenance and truthfully outspoken, a proper man. But his eyes closed in sleep, so they drew away and sat awhile under the trees, until their friend lay quite still. Then they dug a grave under a thorn tree in which little birds sang, and there they laid their friend and companion with his hands crossed on his breast; and while they did that they wept as strong men weep, with dry eyes.

But the peace of the place was broken by the noise of battle, and the sweet smell of the air poisoned by the smoke of fifty fires. For Magellan and Espinosa and sixty men had landed, then had fallen upon the islanders who had nothing with which to defend themselves. So eight of them fell dead, shot with arquebuses, and the rest fled into the land leaving everything. Then the seamen stole all on which they could lay their hands, fruits and household animals and even those things they did not need. Not a house in the village stood unburned. So they called it a great victory, though no seaman or man-at-arms suffered wound or scratch. Yet they feared so greatly an attack in revenge that the fleet sailed without delay.

"These I have looked upon as masters are cowardly dogs after all," said Enrique to Osberne. "I know not at all how I came to see this place before, but see it I did, and well I know the people to be good and kind, not killing, but giving to those who needed, as you have seen."

"But that is no talk for a slave," said Osberne.

"Until now I have been a slave, but now I feel myself to be a slave no longer," answered Enrique. "These are my own people in this part of the world. You shall find that I speak their tongue and they mine. You shall see that they bear themselves bravely, and should not also I? You shall see that these killers of men on the ships shall run as they never fled before."

"Then you know how far it is to the next land, do you?" asked Osberne.

"I know, but I know not how I know," said Enrique. "We shall come to a place of peace and comfort, where there are rich kings and much gold. Think you that I would go on with these who are strangers to me when I find my own people?"

"Then you must see the admiral and tell him what you know," said Osberne.

"For a slave to speak unasked is like a dog that barks in his master's house," said Enrique. "And when the dog is down every dog bites him. So I must know nothing, think nothing, say nothing. Does the admiral strike me, then also strikes Espinosa, and the mate, and the pilot and the pages.

Nor did anyone on the fleet guess at Enrique's knowledge until they found an island called Mazaba, where they anchored.

Out from the shore came fifty canoes, and many praus, all crowded with good-humored natives, suspecting nothing, eager to see the sight; but when they neared the *Trinidad* which lay closest inshore, Enrique ran his eye over them and said to Osberne, " Now is the time. It is my work to see that we have no more of this wicked blood-spilling. I shall warn them in their own speech as you warned men in Patagonia."

" See that you tell them how things are, and see that these on the ships do not understand what you say," Osberne advised. " But play the game fair."

" I shall, and shall tell you what I say," and the slave kept his word for a time, always interpreting later to Osberne what had been said and how things went.

To the surprise of everyone on the ships then Enrique the slave jumped into the rigging and waved his hand, then shouted something at which all the canoes ceased paddling, and what that something was they could not guess. But those in the canoes understood and this is what they heard.

" Come no nearer, these are people who dig pits for the careless. They are not to be trusted in word or in deed. Keep away from them."

Then out broke a great talking in the canoes, some asking questions, some calling on Enrique to tell them more, some talking to his fellow.

On the ship Espinosa turned to Magellan and the mate and the ship-master, for they all stood together. " Now this is a good thing," he said. " The slave knows their tongue and the people — "

" If that be so, then it may be that after all my slave is the first man to go round the world, seeing that he has come to his own place," said Magellan, gloomily.

"The act of the slave is the act of his master," said Espinosa. "Therefore the glory still shall be yours, Admiral. Henceforth, we shall be able to order these natives. With the slave as our tongue, we shall be the easier masters of them all. Our fortunes are made."

Magellan called Enrique to his side. "Tell them," he said, "to bring their king aboard so that we may meet him and do him honor."

What Enrique shouted instead was this: "Come not on the ships though they ask you, and I have been told to tell your king to come. This must be clear between us with no misunderstanding. I shall tell them that you ask them to send some of their own people on shore, and I want to be among them, with one or two whom I know to be of a sort to trust."

So following that speech there arose more clamoring in the canoes, with one man standing up and asking Enrique how he came to be with the ships, as he afterwards told Osberne.

"What do they say?" asked Magellan.

"They will not come on board," answered Enrique. "There have been Moorish ships in these waters, and the Moors have often stolen away their people, so they fear we may do the same. But they ask that you send one or two on shore to receive gifts, and if all goes well then some of them will return to the ships and all shall be understood between us."

With that the officers talked among themselves.

"I would not care to go lest there be treachery, and my duty is with the fleet," said Magellan. "I shall send an envoy and you may be the man, Espinosa."

"Nothing would please me better," said Espinosa. "But a sickness has been upon me for some days and I would be a poor envoy to a king."

"Let me be your envoy," said Pigafetta. "I would see how things and people are, to write in my book. But I would choose those to go who keep out of brawls."

"Whom would you choose?" asked Magellan.

"Your slave, Enrique, to talk for me. Osberne, because I came to know the lad well when he lay sick. Hans, because he has never one face to God and another to the devil," answered Pigafetta.

"Go then," said Magellan. "But return soon."

"Soon enough is well enough," said Pigafetta. "We may be a day and a night. It will not do for you to attack a town because we make our visit long."

"Tell them," ordered Magellan, addressing Enrique, "that we are sending an envoy to their king, and that he must be received in good way or trouble will follow."

So Enrique did what he was told in part, but instead of saying things about trouble, added that when he had the chance he would tell them all. Then Pigafetta and Hans and Osberne went into the skiff, and the canoes laying to this side and that, made a lane in the water down which the skiff rowed and so all got to shore safely.

That day and night stayed long in Pigafetta's memory, so much so that he wrote about it in his book. For a little time Osberne found himself left alone, because Enrique went off with a crowd, all of them laughing and talking. So Osberne wandered about, looking at things from a distance, wondering at the village, and the flowers, and the great butterflies, and the noise of the birds, and the sunshine, and the houses roofed with leaves, and the strange fruits. He saw the chief, or king, a tall man with rings of gold in his ears, and bracelets of gold too; about his head was wrapped a silken cloth, and he wore a silk cloak; in his girdle he carried a dagger with a handle of gold. When Pigafetta bowed, very gravely, the king took him by the hand; and when the Italian waved his hand to Osberne, a chief stepped forward and took the young man by the hand, then all the people set up a great shout of welcome and raised their swords, and daggers, and spears, and shields, high in salute. Then came the great feasting, with roast pork, and fish, and honey, and eggs, and a sweet wine, and birds, and shrimps, and bananas, and strange fruits, and oranges, and coco-nuts, and rice, and ginger. All the while they were eating, with the king and Pigafetta sitting together, and Osberne seated between two chiefs, the king's followers stood behind the diners in two long lines, chanting a song that had no end. Other than that the meal went forward in silence because none knew the speech of the other, and messengers could not find Enrique. But one and the other made signs, and those Pigafetta tried to understand.

" It must be friendliness, though I feared at first he would strike me," said Pigafetta. " But let us do as he does."

What they did, following the action of the chief, was this. With their right hands they took the cup made out of a coco-shell, then made the left hand into a fist and touched the man on the left on his chest with the fist. And before eating a new dish, each man arose from where he had been sitting cross-legged, then raised his hands on high.

" Now I thank the saints that the meal is ended," said Osberne to Pigafetta, when at last the remains of the feast had been carried away.

But Osberne spoke too soon, for while it was true that one meal had ended yet the king sat on his mat and made no move, so the others had to do the same. Nor had they sat in silence very long, before the attendants began to bring in more food, because the king's son had come. So a new meal began with everybody eating as best they could, though Osberne and Pigafetta found small space for new things. That new meal lasted until near darkness, when other attendants came, each with a sort of candle lit, whereupon the king made a sign which Pigafetta said meant that it was time to sleep. The attendants led the two men away to a place where cane mats had been laid under a roof of leaves, and some of them stood around and began to sing a long chant again.

"I could do without the song," said Osberne.

"Well, so also could I," answered Pigafetta. "But let us hope that it is a good song, and if so it is none the worse for being sung twice."

But in spite of the song Osberne yawned a mighty yawn, and went to sleep, and woke thinking he had slept only a few minutes, to see the king with three other notables, and many attendants, Enrique with them.

"These will go with you," explained Enrique. "They wear their best raiment and are all kings, or rajahs. One of them is the King of Sebu and he asks you to go to his place to trade. He will beg the admiral to do so."

"Is there anything else?" asked Pigafetta of Enrique, somewhat suspicious.

"Yes. This King of Sebu says that at Mactan, the place where I was sold to the Moors, lives a traitor rajah whose name is Sila-pula-lapu. But the King of Sebu is the rightful ruler of all that land. If the admiral, my master, will help this king to get his own, then all that the King of Sebu rules will be loyal to Spain."

"Is there anything more?" asked Pigafetta.

"Yes," answered Enrique. "If the admiral will make a trading-place at Sebu, putting on shore the things for trade, then from all parts of the country men will come with gold, and silks, and spices, and rubies, and there will be buying and selling so great that every man in the ship may be rich."

"What think you of this, Osberne?" asked Pigafetta.

"It would be well to go slow," the young man replied. "Were I in the place of the admiral, I would take part in no quarrels. If two dogs do not agree over a bone, the third dog who would settle matters may find himself in a tight place."

"I have nothing to do with it," said Enrique. "I tell to you what this king has said to me."

"But why did he tell you all this?" asked Pigafetta.

"Because I told him of the wonders of the ship, and the cannon, and the cross-bows, and how we have won whenever we fought," answered Enrique.

"Then let us go and see what can be done," said Pigafetta. "We cannot let these stand while we argue. But the whole thing has an ugly look to me."

"It is strange enough," said Osberne as they walked down to the seashore. "Here is the slave Enrique the first man to go round the world. And here, if the admiral lets him be the mouthpiece, is the whole fleet of us at his mercy. I know how it was with the Patagonians, and how I said what I chose with everyone believing."

And on board the *Trinidad* it was much as Osberne feared. Magellan sat on one of two thrones which looked very noble in red and blue cloth, with flags planted here and there, though, as Osberne saw, the thrones were made from casks and planks. To the second throne the King of Sebu was led. Men-at-arms stood around in a half-circle, and the rigging was gay with flags and colored cloth. Enrique stood between Magellan and the native king telling what was said to each in turn. To make a great show the guns were fired, and the seamen sang and beat tambourines and drums. Then two men-at-arms in armor stood and were shot at with arrows which fell from the steel leaving the men unhurt. After that the native nobles were given presents of looking-glasses, and hawk bells, and pieces of glass. Then men hung on the chiefs robes of yellow and white silk, and put red cloth caps on their heads, and threw over their heads necklaces of glass beads. Next they feasted, and while they did so they talked, with Enrique interpreting, and every now and then Espinosa, or Barbosa, or sometimes Magellan, would call out a piece of news.

"Hearest thou that, Pigafetta?" asked Magellan. "This king tells us that all Sebu will be baptized. We shall have the land and its riches."

Another time, when Pigafetta walked across the deck, Espinosa shouted, "What think ye of that, Señor Pigafetta? We are to have enough gold to load a boat!"

Again, when Enrique said something, Barbosa called out for all the ship to hear, "They will give us a pig or a goat for a handful of beads. They will give us gold for iron, and rubies for glass."

Soon men were calling from ship to ship, and boats from the other ships came to the *Trinidad,* so that the decks were thick with men. Then a fever of greed took the sailors. They told one another how rich they would be, and what they would do with the money. And the fever passed into a madness so that some of them danced about, and slapped one another, and even began to sell things which were to be paid for when the gold had been found.

Then Magellan stood up and called for silence, and when the men had quieted down he spoke.

"Now victory is at our hand," he said. "We are at the very door of the Spiceries, which we came to seek. We have found the strait we sought. And now, by the goodness of God, we find a friend in this king who sits with me. A rebel has taken part of his land and he asks us to see justice done. I have given him my word that we will help him. If any man has anything to say against that, let him speak."

Then Joao Serrao stood forth and raised his hand. " Say I, let us not interfere in the quarrels of others. Make me a prisoner if you will, but I say that it is foolishness to take part in the troubles of others and in this I am against you, though I shall obey to the end."

But Serrao's speech found few who favored it.

" Then what of our gold? " asked one.

" Have we come thus far and suffered as we have, to sail on and on, going back to Spain in rage and misery? " asked Nicholas the Greek.

" Run away, Serrao, as your brother did," said another.

" A bashful dog never fattens," cried out a page.

" Hold your tongue, Serrao," cried another page, and men laughed and bade Serrao sit down.

" I have said my say," said Serrao. " But there are times when it does not become a man to hold his tongue."

" And I," said Espinosa, " am for the admiral. Here for our help we get the trade we came for, the land we sought, the gold and treasure we want. This is our crowning day. You spit against heaven if you turn against this fortune that has come to us."

Then the King of Sebu stood up and talked, though no one

except Enrique understood, and when he had sat down again Magellan called upon the slave to interpret.

"He says that in Sebu you shall all grow rich with trading," said Enrique. "He says that in Sebu the people will come by hundreds and thousands to be baptized in the Christian faith. He says that at sight of the ships and the men-at-arms the followers of the false ruler will fly to the jungle without striking a blow."

"I am for our great general!" shouted a page.

"The sorry thing is that it is the blood of the fighters that makes the general great," said Hans to Osberne.

"A sorrier thing is that I fear Enrique, the slave, is looking for his freedom and his revenge too," said Osberne, behind his hand. "And to think that he learned the tricks of how to interpret to suit himself, from me."

"Well, we can do nothing," said Hans. "As the master so the work."

And so it came about that the fleet sailed for Sebu.

CHAPTER XI

How Espinosa Won

S O THEY reached Sebu and there a mighty trading began. They made a market place on the edge of the
jungle where parrots chattered and insects chirped, and
where birds yellow and blue and scarlet and gold-green
fluttered about and in and out of the selling stalls; where mon-
keys chattered and butterflies danced in the air, and frogs
croaked. Richard of Normandy, the carpenter, got out from
the hold the planks and timbers saved from the wrecked *San-*

tiago and built trading booths out of them which the natives roofed with leaves. All the while the islanders sat on the ground watching, and among them went Enrique the slave telling them, by Magellan's orders, what wonders would come to pass, and how great and mighty the men of the fleet were. Richer folk from the back country walked about dressed in silken garments, some of them with jewels and gold-handled daggers and scimitars and rings of gold as befitting their state. The pages found bright colored stuff with which they draped the booths, so that in the bright light, and with the million flowers and blossomed trees, and with the white sea sand and the blue sea, and with the strange sweet smell that came from the jungle, it seemed to Osberne more gay than a fair at Portsdown. Yet he could not bring himself to feel at ease, much less to be as gay as some of his shipmates, for he feared what the slave might be saying and planning, feared the more because the King of Sebu had so much to say and to do with Enrique.

"What I fear is that he may be planning a revenge for all that he has suffered," said Osberne to Hans.

"Have you tried to tell Magellan or Pigafetta what you fear?"

"It is no use. I cannot get to Magellan. The Señor Pigafetta lends me an ear, but he tells me that the admiral is full of a plan to help this Sebu against the king with the long name," answered Osberne.

"But how feels Pigafetta about it?" asked Hans. "He is a wise head."

"He laughs and says that while there may be a plot yet a mischievous plot may bring a good end," said Osberne. "As for the men, they see gain and forget pain. Even Serrao will

BARTER

say nothing against the plan now. I spoke to him an hour ago and he shrugged his shoulders and said, " One foolish act may undo a man, but a timely one may make his fortune." Then he added, " But for all that a man should not stick his nose in his neighbor's pot."

" In days of money-making I believe that men lose their senses," said Hans, then fell to working. So each went his way, Osberne to help bring ashore the things for trading, and Hans to prepare the guns to fire a grand salvo when the trading should commence. And when the shadows swept the market place, when the guns thundered and the seamen beat their drums, then the fair was opened. Nor was stranger fair ever held, with seamen wearing swords for shop-keepers, and rajahs all a-glitter with gold and precious stones buying glass beads that would have sold in Portsdown for a penny, but paying rubies and gold for them. Sailors sold their old shoes for gold rings that would have bought clothes fit for a grandee. One fellow gave a broken cup for a ruby. A page bought a pig and a dagger for a playing card. The natives weighed gold against iron, in balances made of a spear shaft.

" Saw man ever such trading since the world began? " Osberne heard Robert of Normandy say to Antonio Ros. " As I live, they are giving fifteen ducats of gold for fourteen pounds of iron. And I myself exchanged a bent nail for a pearl."

" And I," said Antonio, " exchanged a cloth cap for two rubies."

As for Osberne, who stood behind a stall on which were hawk bells, and colored kerchiefs and fishhooks, he felt something like shame at the trading when he saw the pile of jewels, and gold arm rings, and precious stones, and cloaks made of feathers that were given to him in exchange for trash. So presently people walked around as if they had dressed for a silly show, grave rajahs with old sea-boots thrust on their feet, women wearing greasy and ragged old coats, old men with white hair tricked out with looking-glasses and glass beads, sailors with gold bracelets about their wrists and ankles, and carrying spears or a kris. Two pages, helped by natives, were trying to drive a herd of twenty pigs down to the boats, and for the pigs they had paid two iron knives. A rich man of the islands walked about proudly dressed in a flowing garment of ten ells of cheap red cloth for which he had given a piece of gold as well as his own clothes of silk. Other natives had hung strange things about themselves as ornaments; scissors, hatchets, kerchiefs and fishhooks. And everywhere sailors were eating heartily of fruits, or of meats cooked by the natives. Magellan himself went about with a large pair of gold earrings, and two bracelets of gold, and anklets set with precious stones, all of which had been given to him by the King of Sebu.

On the day after the great fair, which was a Sunday, came the receiving of the people into the church. For Enrique had told Magellan how their hearts were touched and how nothing would do but that the king and his followers should be baptized. So across the market place went a grand procession, with Magellan and his officers walking after a standard-bearer, then, following them, forty men-at-arms, next sailors beating tamborines, and after that all others. And not only the king, and his son, and his nephew, and fifty followers were baptized, but other rajahs; and when the news spread, all and sundry of the natives, to the number of twenty-two hundred, came to be made Christians. Also there came, presently, a few chiefs who were not favorable to the King of Sebu and they too were baptized and then allowed to trade. But one of them soon

changed his mind and laughed at the king, at least so Enrique
said when the chief had gone. Magellan, very angry, sent out
after them a force of men-at-arms who killed a few and burnt
their village to ashes.

"And that," said Hans, " is a strange way to spread the news
of good-will and peace on earth."

" But there is to be more," said Osberne. " We are to fight
the Sebu fight, so Enrique tells me. Serrao opposes it, but
Magellan is all for it. The two men came to high words, I am
told, with Magellan saying to Serrao that a man of good blood
snuffs the fight as a true-bred hound scents the trail of its
quarry."

" And what said Serrao to that? " asked Hans.

" There is where the high words came. He answered, 'You
come of good blood and so also does a black pudding,' " said
Osberne. " The rest I know nothing of because Enrique was
sent away so that the two might quarrel in quiet."

" This affair is a stratagem laid by the devil with the slave
for his messenger," said Hans. " Mark my words, evil must
come of it. There is neither sense nor common gain to be got
from fighting."

Those last words Osberne remembered when the fleet came
to Mactan to fight the rebel king. With the ships went the King
of Sebu and a thousand canoes, the natives making a great noise
of shouting, and a vast to-do shaking their spears of wood,
which, like the arms of the rebels, were nothing but sticks with
the ends charred in the fire. On board the *Trinidad,* when they
had anchored, all men could hear what went on in the way of
talk between the captains.

" It is not our quarrel," argued Serrao, not softening his
voice in the least. " Let this Sebu do his fighting if he wants

to fight, and we can turn the battle, if needed, at the last. We have no men to lose."

"Not so," answered Magellan. "We are to rule these lands, and this Sebu and his men may look on and see how we can fight."

Then Serrao flew into a rage. "It is only a fool who would leave a safe shelter to step out into a storm," he cried. "Some day a nation wiser than ours, with a wiser ruler, will come to these rich islands."

"That is an insult," answered Magellan, no less angry. "But what of the men? See you not that they are all for the battle?"

"He who would make a fool of himself will always find many to help him," retorted Serrao.

"Now you shall pay for those words," said Magellan.

"If an insult makes you open your eyes, then better the insult than flattery that would close them," answered Serrao. "Look on the shore. As I live there are more than a thousand men. Let Sebu and his thousand fight them, if there must be a fight, and let us look on and see how they battle."

"What costs little is little esteemed," retorted Magellan. "We shall show with what small force we conquer. With sixty men I, mark you, shall beat the enemy. Even you, Serrao, shall not help. Nay. I shall do it with less than sixty. Four dozen is enough and the rest of the sixty may stay in the boats under the charge of the gunner Hans. Pigafetta, you may come with me."

"Now let me counsel—" began Serrao, but Magellan stopped him.

"Give neither counsel nor salt until you are asked for it," Magellan said, and turned his back on Serrao.

Because of the strange madness in the man matters went in

a mad way. Osberne with eleven others had to stay in the
boats which lay off shore, while Magellan and his four dozen
men waded to the land, so Osberne saw all that was to be seen,
nor could he or the others at any time lift a hand to help. He
saw the King of Sebu and his thousand natives in their many
canoes. They were looking on and laughing and shouting,
much as people watch a show made for their pleasure.

No sooner had the four dozen with Magellan set foot on
shore than down from the jungle came a cloud of natives running, stopping now and then to steady themselves to throw
stones or sticks. But they threw so well and with such force
that some of the Spaniards staggered when struck. When
some of the seamen shot arrows the shafts were caught by the
natives. One of the lances thrown by the natives took Pigafetta in the cheek so that he fought no more that day. Another
pierced the eye of the *Victoria's* gunner and entered his brain,
so that he fell dead. Then all seemed muddled, with men
running and fighting, until, at a lull, those on the boats heard
a shout that rang above the noise, when Magellan cried, "Fire
the village!"

Then all the Spaniards ran up the beach, leaving the
wounded Pigafetta and the dead gunner, and the natives fled
into the jungle, so that it looked as if the battle was won. But
no sooner were the reed houses ablaze than out of the trees and
tall grasses came the islanders placing themselves so that the
Spaniards were between them and the smoke and flame, and
so cut off from the sea.

"Saints! What folly is this, with us here and unable to fire
our guns?" said Hans.

"Let us row to shore and do what we can," said another, and
for that everyone was willing, so they started.

Meanwhile on shore matters went swiftly. The Spaniards were ringed about by natives, and the fight waxed hotter. Soon the circle of natives opened, and a crowd of fighting, struggling men in armor thickly beset by the enemy broke off from the rest. At one time a man-at-arms would run down the beach towards the sea, but stones were showered thickly and he would fall. Then the wind changed and from the burning village came a cloud of thick black smoke that hid the fight from those who watched from the ships. When the smoke cleared some saw Magellan with his sword drawn, his back to the sea, and his face to his foes. All the while a great noise of shouting and screaming mingled with the noise of guns, for those on the ships fired, but they had to fire into the air because they dared not train their guns low lest they wound or kill their own men, such was the confusion. Some saw a native thrust his lance into Magellan's throat, and some saw the admiral stab in return, but a crowd of men leaped into the fight and no more could be seen except a great struggle of men with nothing very clear or sharp cut; some running, some falling, some rolling away out of the fight. Nor until the boats landed and the men jumped out on shore did the natives retreat a little way, though they did not go far, but stood near the village ready to fight should the boatmen attack. But what those in the boats sought was an end to the struggle, and the safety of their companions. Yet only forty came out of the fray alive, and many of those beaten and bruised and wounded, while of the killed there were seven, and Magellan one of them. So ended the battle of Mactan on the twenty-seventh day of April, of the year fifteen hundred and twenty-one, and thus died Ferdinand Magellan, gallantly but foolishly.

Sadly enough the boats pulled back to the ships and lifted

their men on board, Pigafetta moaning, all the while, his face
deadly white, and saying over and over again, " We have lost
our mirror, our light, our comforter, our true guide." No other
man of the fleet seemed to care overmuch. Death and pain
and treachery were close neighbors and had been so for a long
time, therefore almost they minded grief not at all and took
trouble for granted. But many a one said that had the words
of Serrao been heeded the battle would never have been fought
and all would have gone well.

The sayings grew into murmurs, and into plottings, so that
on the fleet men told one another, " It is Serrao who should
be our admiral," or they asked, " are you for Serrao?" Some
bolder, said, " Let us go in a body and declare for Serrao." So,
before an hour had passed, the rumor ran from mouth to
mouth that Serrao would take Magellan's place. But never
were the men more surprised than when Espinosa called all
hands together and made a speech in which he said that he
favored Serrao above all men as a navigator, an honest man, a
wise leader and a good companion, therefore spoke for him
as admiral.

Then Serrao stood up, very bold, very determined, very outspoken.

" I shall take command," he said, and while saying looked
angrily at Espinosa, " but Barbosa must be my partner in the
matter. I want men I can trust. I fear the voyage not at all,
but I do fear all this plotting. There is too much secret planning. There is too much whispering. There is strange secrecy.
There are whispering tongues that poison truth. Those I cannot fight against. I like not these messages given to the natives
by the mouth of that slave Enrique. I always feared the way
Magellan believed Enrique the slave. I like not nonsense such

as this trading and folly at Sebu. A man may grow great in well-doing, but he grows little in meanness. I cannot get these things that I tell you into any fine order. I speak roughly and as thoughts come to my mind, for I am a sailor and no man of the court. But mark this, and mark it well. Here I stand, your chosen commander. I have no ear for any man's praise. Many here carry hate in their hearts for me, and all men hate those they have wronged, for that is the devil's work to go from wrong-doing to evil-doing, and then, perchance, to murder. So I say to those who plot — " and his small eyes looked like slits.

"Name the names of these plotters," called out Carvalho. "Name them, Serrao, so that we may all beware of them. I call on you. Have no fear."

"I will name them," answered Serrao. "First then I name you, Carvalho, as one from whom I shall guard my gates. Second I name you, Espinosa, as a whisperer and a man with a forked tongue whose heart is full of poison. And as your tool, I name Magellan's slave, Enrique. So watch, all men, that Enrique goes not ashore in any boat. Watch when whisperers get their heads together, for a whisper separates friends. And he who whispers lies. But remember this. I am in command and what I order is to be done. Now for my orders. We shall sail to Sebu and pick up all that trappery of trade. Then we shall set a straight course for Spain and so end the matter."

"But the body of our dead admiral. What of that? Shall we not seek it and punish his murderers?" called out Robert of Normandy.

"All that evil is fairly buried," answered Serrao. "We shall not stir it up. We sow evil and reap sorrow. Enough. Now we sail."

So presently they came to Sebu again, and men were sent ashore to take down the booths, and put on board the trading things, and to bring away those who had been left behind to look out for trade.

Now Osberne, having worked on shore in the morning, went again on board the *Trinidad,* to dress the wounds of the men hurt in the battle of Mactan, and also to carry food and water to the slave Enrique, who, for safety's sake and that he might be kept from his own people, had been locked in a cell in the hold. Having done that duty he went on deck, then found himself at a loss because of not being sure whether he had safely locked the door of the cell, though he felt that he had done so. So he went down to the dark hold again, his bare feet making no more noise than a cat would, and, putting his hand to the lock found no key there, wherefore his heart sank because he feared that from some slip of the mind on his part the slave might have gotten out. Yet he remembered having left everything safe. So, greatly fearing, he stood stock still, holding his breath, trying to hear some sound from within, as of the slave moving. But what was his amazement to hear the sound of voices, whispering. He knew them to be the voices of Espinosa and of Carvalho, with Enrique saying something now and then.

" So make no mistake," he heard Espinosa say. " We shall stay here on the ship. You, Enrique, must swim ashore. You must seek out the king and his chiefs.

" But not a word to anyone," said Carvalho, gruffly. " One word on the ship and you get your throat slit. Do this well and you have your freedom. Remember, though Magellan is dead you are still the slave of his wife. But do this well that I tell you to do, and you may be a free man."

"This is what you must do," went on Espinosa. "You must tell the king to prepare a feast and then invite all the captains to partake of it. But you must also tell him that the most of the captains and officers are here to — " Then what was said Osberne did not hear because of a stirring about in the cell. Later he heard this said, "good men and true who will sail away and leave his land in peace if we are rid of trouble makers. Now is all that clear?"

"It is all clear," answered the slave. "I shall do it all."

"But having given your message to the king," the voice went on, "swim back again to the ship and get on board without noise. Carvalho or I shall wait on deck. Then get back to this cell where if all goes well I shall be, and when the kings and chiefs come, then you shall be let out to tell what they say."

"And remember," began Carvalho, though what the slave had to remember Osberne did not hear. For at that instant the bolt moved in the lock and the door opened, so Osberne fled. But from a dark place he saw Carvalho and Espinosa come out, then saw them lock the door leaving the slave inside.

Osberne knew that he could not make known what he had heard, because both Serrao and Barbosa were on board the *Concepcion,* and Pigafetta, all fevered from his hurt, was too sick a man to understand. The best thing seemed to be to keep watch on the cell so that the slave should not escape, and that watching he commenced. But he had not been long when Espinosa came.

"What is this?" Espinosa asked. "What do you here when others are at work?"

Osberne could see his eyes aflame. He also saw that Espinosa laid his hand, as if in carelessness, on his dagger. Plainly it would not do to raise trouble.

"I have to see to the slave between whiles, as well as to the sick," answered Osberne.

"And have you seen your charges lately?" came the next question.

"All except the slave," said Osberne.

"Then open the door and look to him now," ordered Espinosa.

So Osberne threw open the door and they both looked in, seeing Enrique asleep, as it seemed.

"There is water. There is bread. And the slave sleeps," said Espinosa. "So you may be gone after you have locked the door. And remember what Serrao warned about spying and plotting. This looks bad. And now, all being done, you may row me in the skiff to the *Victoria*."

"But —" began Osberne.

"But me no buts," said Espinosa. "Serrao said orders must be obeyed. We go first to the *Concepcion* where I would see the Admiral Serrao."

There being nothing for it but to obey orders Osberne brought the skiff round to the ship's side and held it while Espinosa stepped in, then he put his back to the oars. But Osberne, as he rowed, could hardly keep his eyes from the fox-face of the man, and the man, in his turn, often looked at Osberne.

When they had gone a little distance Espinosa said, with what Osberne thought to be craftiness, "As I remember when we were in Patagonia, you did much to keep the men and the Indians from bloodshed. At the time I did not see as I see now. But the Patagonians were no great matter, having no souls to save. With these it is different. They have been baptized and are proper men. It is my wish to have no more killing. I have often wished that you knew the language of these people as you did those of Patagonia."

To that Osberne found nothing to say. Nor did Espinosa say anything for a while, but let his hand dabble in the water, looking far away, though sometimes casting a quick glance at Osberne. That made Osberne think that somehow Espinosa suspected him of having heard the talk with the slave.

"I saw the slave this day," went on Espinosa. "Carvalho and I together saw him. We were asking him questions. For, you see, what you were in the Patagones, he is here, in a sort of way. It seems that because of the baptism the king wishes to give a farewell feast. I would that it were a love feast so that the Admiral Serrao could know me as a friend and a well-wisher. There have been slanderers who have poisoned his mind. Unhappily I have not been well liked. Even you, for a time, had no love for me."

He laughed as he ended, but it was a laugh from the teeth outwards. All that Osberne could find to say, was, "I wish that there could be peace for the rest of the voyage." But he thought, as he spoke, that his suspicions would sound silly if voiced, but yet his fear and suspicion stayed strong within him.

"Carvalho, a rough man and a true, has told the slave that his throat would be slit if he said anything other than what makes for peace," said Espinosa. "We were in the prison cell talking," he added. Then he shot a question suddenly. "Tell me, how do the natives take it since we stopped trading?"

"Not knowing their tongue I cannot say for truth. But they seem not to like the taking away of the booths and the trinkets," answered Osberne.

" As I feared. Just as I feared," said Espinosa. " I have wondered if Enrique could swim ashore and see the king, telling him how it would be if something could be arranged for friendship. I think I shall propose something of the sort of Serrao. Enrique must seem to act on his own accord."

Osberne heard and was struck amazed to see how things seemed slipping away from him. He was left with nothing to say. The very things that had seemed most secret were being said aloud.

" You remember that I was the first to name Serrao as captain," went on Espinosa. " There is a mischief-maker in the fleet who has a burden to lift from his soul. I wish I knew the sinner."

Osberne had to bite his tongue to keep himself from shouting out, " Liar! False traitor! You know you are plotting craftily."

So they came to the ship, and as Espinosa stood up he said to Osberne, " Well, be of good cheer! The gallows takes it own at the last." Then he climbed aboard and Osberne was left to wait until he came again. Like a song the words ran in his mind, " I have been outwitted! I have been outwitted! " And while he waited the minutes went into hours, so that the stars were out long before the officers found themselves ready to go back to the *Trinidad.*. But he found that he was not to go back with the rest to the flagship, for he heard Espinosa say to Serrao, " Set your heart at rest, Admiral. I shall go to the *Victoria* and see that all is well."

" Who rows your boat? " asked Serrao in his blunt way.

" The lad Osberne," answered Espinosa.

" Tell San Martin and the priest Pedro de Valderrama of

your change of heart, and come to the flagship when you have done so," said Serrao.

So Osberne, wondering much at the strange plot, set himself to his oars sturdily the sooner to get the work done and out of the way, but it was long past midnight before he set foot on the deck of the *Trinidad*. First he went to the cell and there found the slave Enrique seeming to be asleep. Yet when Osberne laid his hand on the man's head he found his hair wet.

" How is this? " asked Osberne.

" I drank and somehow slipped and fell as I did so, and the water splashed all about. You may see for yourself how the floor is still wet," said the slave, pointing to wet spots.

But Osberne put the tip of his wet finger to his lips, then said, " But you do not drink sea water. This is salt. You lie like a coward. I believe you have been ashore. Confess."

" Little they care what they give a slave," answered Enrique and laid himself down as if to sleep again. " They gave me sea water to drink. And how could I, a prisoner, get ashore? "

" Every lie has ten for a witness," said Osberne, and went away in high dudgeon because of the way he had been fooled. With mischief afoot and on the scent of it, he could find no trail to follow.

And the next morning there was proof positive of the mischief brewing. At sunrise there were canoes with kings and chiefs in them at the ship's side. There was a canoe loaded with fruit. There were presents of gold and jeweled things. There were flowers, and spices, and pigs, and birds. And on the deck Serrao and Barbosa and Espinosa smiled, and talked, and made signs. So up came the natives, not keeping together but going about among the seamen, making their signs of friendship and having their hands shaken by the Spaniards.

Then pages made a throne of casks and boards, which they covered with cloths and flags, and men-at-arms came up, all very fine in armor and with their swords and spears. Even the sick men came on deck. And when a chief began to make a speech, Serrao called for Enrique, and the slave was brought up and carried himself proudly, like a man of importance.

" Tell us what is said and speak the truth," said Serrao, and at that all eyes were on the slave.

" The king tells you he is for friendship," said Enrique when the chief had come to an end. " His people have prepared a feast and he invites all the captains and officers. At that feast he will give over his lands to the King of Spain. He will also give a present, asking Admiral Serrao to carry it to his king. And there are a thousand and more to be baptized, wherefore he asks that the priest should go on shore with the rest."

" Ask him why is all this," said Serrao, who was not without his suspicion though he could put his finger on nothing wrong.

" Because the men of the fleet have tried to do what they could to bring the chief at Mactan to order, and because in doing that the admiral lost his life. So this king would show honor to those who remain, as he would have honored the Admiral Magellan had he not died." Thus answered Enrique, as if telling what the chief had said.

" Now I say that these simple folk have not the wit to plot anything," said Barbosa. " We have heard how Columbus went on shore and safely met the natives, and what he dared to do we may do. I am for going, but not for staying long."

" And I," said San Martin.

" I also," cried Espinosa.

" And also I," called out Carvalho. " There is another thing for you all. Lest there should be treachery and trouble, and so that all may be ready for flight if need be, I myself shall look to it that the way is clear, for I shall stay with the boats on the shore. I warrant that there will be small chance for any savage who should try to play tricks."

Hearing that Osberne was like a man dazed. Everything pointed to trouble and treachery, but there seemed to be nothing on which he could lay a hand, so how his suspicions could be made clear he could not see. That Enrique had been on shore privately he felt sure, but there was no way to prove it. And if he had been on shore, then his purpose had been to have dealings with his own people there. It was also certain that Espinosa had some secret business with the slave, but then Espinosa had the ear of Serrao and had told a tale to suit himself, so how could any words that came from Osberne count? Nor was there anything to prove that if Enrique had dealings with his own people those dealings were treacherous. The thought flashed through Osberne's mind that even if he did stand up and shout all that he suspected, he would be looked upon as no more than a laughing-stock. But worst of all was the knowledge that Espinosa had it in his mind to be admiral of the fleet some day, by hook or by crook, even if men and officers were sacrificed to that end. As for himself, suspicion was not dead among some that in Patagonia he had been a deserter from the fleet who had gone to live with natives. So with it all, Osberne's tongue was tied.

"Well, if we are to go, then the sooner the better," said Serrao, impatient as always. "I have no love for this feasting, but there lies the thing to be done for the king. It is clear that we cannot plant the Standard of Spain on the land if we stay on the ship. So let us get to shore."

Carvalho is in charge of this boat and Espinosa in charge of the other," ordered Pedro, the mate, and named six men to row each boat.

Then up stood Sebastian del Cano, a man thoughtful and proud, and began calling on them to act with care. " Is this a fleet with a commander, or is it a rabble? " he asked. " Is it an orderly thing with a head, or is it a monster with many heads? Serrao, I call on you. You have been wise, but no man is so wise but that he may slip sometimes."

For a moment some of them paused, for there was mastery in del Cano, but wisdom fled when one man shouted, " Are we to have nothing for our pains? " and another cried, " Is it to be always the ship and nothing but the ship? " Others called out that it was time to get rich. So, laughing, and not heeding del Cano, they crowded into the boats and into the canoes and pushed for shore, white men and brown making a great show of friendship.

From the ship men saw them land. They saw natives by the hundreds come down to the canoes and boats. They saw them waving, and heard them laughing and shouting as the party went up the beach. There were shouts from those who went with the natives, and there were answering shouts from Espinosa and Carvalho and those who stayed with the boats. When the party ashore reached the market place it split into two parts, that in which walked the priest going to the jungle, the other with Serrao making for the hill.

" That has an evil look," Osberne heard Sebastian del Cano say to his page, at a time when Osberne bent over Pigafetta to give him water, for the wounded man had climbed on deck to rest awhile in the sun. Then, as it seemed, all at once every-one on the ship gave a cry of astonishment. For ashore things had flashed into fight, with a terrible shouting and screaming.

Some had fallen on the priest and on Martin, the map maker, with their spears and knives. The other party was a tanglement of men thrusting and stabbing. Now and then a sword or a piece of armor glittered in the sun, but the light went out like a candle snuffed. Carvalho and Espinosa roaring, "Make ready to fire! Make ready the guns!"

Then, swift and terrible, out of the jungle came more natives who swept down upon the Serrao party so that those on the ships saw nothing but a staggering, struggling mass. But Serrao broke away, thrusting and slashing with his sword, and many a man went down.

"Get ready and fire!" said Sebastian del Cano to Hans. "I am no officer, but obey. Fire high, and at the crowd on the jungle edge."

The bombards thundered and on shore men began to fall, and many to run. But some made a rush for Serrao. Others came out of the jungle from another direction. So Serrao ran down to the water's edge, though lances were thrown at him, then went into the sea and turned again to face the savages. One, a great fellow with a kris, ran at the captain with a mighty splashing of water, but Serrao's sword went through his body and he fell. And above the noise some on the ship heard Serrao cry, "Rescue! Rescue! Would you leave us?"

By that time Espinosa and Carvalho had gained the deck and were roaring orders as if they had been madmen. Then Osberne and others saw the vile treachery of it all, and saw how everything had been prepared to lift anchor and set sail.

"You dogs and sons of dogs!" roared Sebastian del Cano, shaking his fist at Espinosa. "You treacherous and black-hearted swine! Would you leave a companion thus?"

"Arrest this fellow!" shouted Espinosa to some men-at-arms, and at the command they leveled their pikes at the knight's breast, and he, being unarmed, and long since robbed of his weapons, had nothing to do but to stand or else die.

So the ships moved before the wind and the figures on shore shrank to specks, and twenty-seven good men's lives were sacrificed to the ambition of black-hearted Espinosa of Seville who swore that he, some day, would be admiral of the fleet. And when the men were counted it was found that of the two hundred and seventy who sailed from Spain, only a hundred and fifteen were left.

That counting was done on the evening of the day of the great treachery when the three ships lay off the island of Bohol, and when Espinosa and Carvalho had gathered the men together.

"It is clear," said Espinosa, "that we have not enough men to handle three ships, but only two. As admiral I seek counsel from all men, giving ear to any man if he be loyal. But let no mutinous dog open his mouth on pain of death."

"What says Sebastian del Cano?" asked Carvalho, for the knight had been brought under guard, though not in chains, to the deck.

"Give me the ship you cannot work, and let me have ten men, and I ask no more," said the knight.

"You do not address me in proper manner," said Espinosa. "I am your admiral and thus I am to be called."

"If you crave honor, then I salute you as admiral, I who deserve honor and have it not, to you who have it and deserve it not," answered del Cano. "But I bid you go the true road to honor, dear Admiral, that road being the way of conduct and courage. Go that way if you can. But some never tread the way of honor."

" Say no more to him," said Carvalho to Espinosa. " You will only end in sending men to his side."

But Espinosa thrust Carvalho aside then shook his fist in del Cano's face. " Beware," he shouted, " lest you be honored with what you deserve, which is a rope and death."

" Honor often blossoms on the grave," answered del Cano quietly and, hearing that, more than one man began to call out for del Cano, praising him.

" Give him a ship and let him try," shouted one.

" And I offer to go with him," shouted Hans.

" And I," said Osberne.

Others called from the crowd.

" It shall not be," shouted Espinosa. " These are my orders. The *Concepcion* is old and leaky. We have enough men for the *Victoria* and the *Trinidad*.. I shall take the *Victoria,* Carvalho shall captain the *Trinidad*. The *Concepcion* shall be burnt. I shall not give it up to any man. These are my orders. And now for you who stay true. We have hungered and we have suffered. We are in rags. But we shall go back to Spain under my command, I promise you, all well laden with riches. From this time forth we take what we get, towns, ships, slaves, gold, anything. Here is no law. We shall sail the seas as pirates, taking what comes our way. We shall do as Ochali did, raiding and pillaging. We shall be strong as Barbarossa of Barbary. I promise every man as much gold as he can carry ashore at Seville. And our companion, Carvalho, who has knowledge of such matters, shall tell you how things will be. Tell them Carvalho."

So Carvalho stood up, and many of the men gave a great

shout, for although he was a rascal, they yet knew him to be bold. Also many were glad to know that some one would lead who promised them riches. There was the hope of adventure too, after all that miserable trouble.

"Now hear me," said Carvalho. "I ran with some free companions to Brazil, and there had a merry time. This son of mine who is with us, is the first of white skin to be born in the Americas. We sacked towns with our ships, and we got gold and precious stones. We had no master. We lived a merry life. We returned to Spain rich men, and the riches of those who died we shared among the living. It is a good life, the pirate's life. And little pirates are hanged, but great pirates are honored. We shall be great pirates. But to pirate in good fashion there needs be laws among pirates. So I have drawn up laws and you shall hear them if you will."

"Read," shouted one.

"Give us your laws," called another.

"Let us hear," shouted many.

"And be not too great in punishment," said one, at which a laugh went up.

"This is the first law then," began Carvalho, and he read. "*One half of what is taken to be shared between captains and pilots and gunners, the other half to go to the men.*"

"The carpenters should share with the captains and pilots," said Robert of Normandy.

"No. All shall share alike," put in another, and a roar went up, "share all alike."

"So be it then," said Carvalho. "We all share alike. But come to the other laws. The second is this. Hear it. *If any man run away or keep any secret from the companions, then he shall be set ashore as Juan de Cartagena was.*"

"Agreed!" said several.

"Then belike we shall soon lose our captains, if keeping treasure secret be counted a crime," cried out a page.

"The third law is that *If any man steal he shall be hanged,*" went on Carvalho.

"For your own safety, Carvalho, make the hanging to be by the belt, not by the neck. Otherwise we may lose you, our Admiral, very soon," called out a man-at-arms.

"Long live the admirals of the pirates!" shouted another, laughing.

"Next," said Carvalho, grinning broadly, "*If any man steal from another, or takes another's share wrongfully to the value of a maravedi, he shall be beheaded.*"

"So we shall lose our captains in almost no time," cried a sailor, and again a laugh went up.

Then Carvalho folded up his paper. "There are more laws and good ones," he said. "But some of you choose to laugh, and a measly hog spoils the stye as the saying goes, so as this is serious I will read no more. Besides, a starved belly has no ears. But we begin our companionship with a great feast, then we burn the old *Concepcion,* and after that, on we go to riches."

And so things went. They feasted on board the *Concepcion,* with much laughter and merriment, and at the end they burned the ship.

But some stayed on board the *Trinidad,* caring nothing for that sort of riot, among them Osberne and Hans. And it was common talk among those who stayed that sooner or later some wise head must be chosen to take the ships, and the earlier the better. Sebastian del Cano, who sat apart, for he rarely talked with the men, holding himself an aristocrat and of better blood,

went on burnishing his armor. When the men's talk came
to an end he called to Osberne.

" There is something I would say," he said. " But first know
that I am no plotter."

" I have not thought you to be that," answered Osberne.

" You are a seaman? "

" I sailed with my master, Sir Robert," answered Osberne.

" Good. Now hear this. As we sail on and on it seems that
by some evil fate we kill those with brains and good-will.
These, your captains, often come to me to know something of
navigation. Did I not know that art and science then I would
have lost my life long since. But who can tell the day or the
hour when they may destroy me in their madness? And that
madness is a sort of leprosy that grows in this fleet. What I
would do then is to teach you something of the art of navigation, so that if I die there may be a chance that something of
this shall be saved. Do you read, Osberne? "

" Yes."

" And write? "

" Yes."

" Know you anything of the mathematics? "

" Something."

" Go forth then and do your best, keeping out of the filth all
about. There will be times when I can instruct you and that
I shall do. This knavery may serve for awhile, but order must
come in the long run and then, if I live no longer, you must
do what you can."

" This is a kindness," began Osberne, but the knight stopped
him with a raised hand.

" It is no kindness," he said, sternly. " I do not give you
learning so that you may be a companion for me, but to the

end that you may be a better companion for yourself. Soon these rogues must disagree, then honesty may have a chance. And there is this. If ever you come to your own country, I bid you say to your master that Sebastian del Cano, gentleman, sends him greetings, for it is a good master that makes a good man."

Then the knight fell to polishing his armor again, so Osberne went.

CHAPTER XII

The Casting of the Dice

FOR MANY years after, Osberne sometimes awoke in the night thinking that he was still in the middle of that time of sea-robber work, so deep a mark did it all leave on him. There were fearful things done — the burning of houses and villages, robbery and theft, the deafening noise of cannon in quiet places, the capturing of ships, and the killing of men. In the quiet of the night, long afterwards, he would hear the noise of the ship crashing into native boats, the cries of wounded men drowning, the shouts of shipmates bent on murder. But there were some quiet days in those fearful times when Osberne and del Cano sat in a cabin, and when the knight instructed the Portsdown sailor in navigation, so that he came to be able to know in what part of the world they sailed, and to find his way, and to tell how far this place lay from that. Also he came to know something of map making. But those hours of learning were rare, for the pirate-hearted Carvalho would have none of them.

Once Carvalho came up and would have snatched the book away, a book of navigation that the knight held doubly precious because it had been made by a man named Faliero, in Spain, a great scholar; but the knight stood up, his eyes ablaze. "Dolt and driveler!" he said, "another such move and you come to your journey's end. That end is near enough. Beware lest I bring it nearer."

The next day they were sailing with a light wind along the coast of Borneo. The *Victoria,* steered by Osberne, rounded a point, and at anchor in a little bay they saw a very noble junk, its sails of silk, its hull shining. So Carvalho gave the order to steer close, to the end that news might be had. But what was the surprise of the seamen, when they drew near, to see a boat well furnished, with men in rich dress, and one in particular finely clad, a young man of pleasant manner. In friendly way the master of the junk stood up and said something, which the page Gubileto interpreted as asking from whence the ships came.

"Ask them if they would like to come on board and see the wonders of the ship," said Carvalho, and the page obeyed, then told what the young man said in return.

It was this:

"Indeed I would be glad to visit you, for friendship's sake. I shall be glad to take a meal with you, or to have you take a meal with me. But the wonders of ships have grown old, and I wonder at them no more, having seen so many in Molucca."

" Come on board then and rest awhile. You shall have good welcome, and meat and drink, and what of presents you choose," said Carvalho, through the mouth of the page.

" We are not weary," answered the young man. " And also we are near our journey's end."

" Well, let us be merry awhile together," said Carvalho.

So the young man swung himself lightly on to the deck of the *Victoria,* and two lads who seemed to be his servants followed him, then stood somewhat apart. Now to the young man Carvalho looked like a seaman, and no very clean one, for he was dirty and unshaven, and his clothes were ill-worn. But Sebastian del Cano, who stood by the mast, was a man clean and well-trimmed as to beard, neat too as to clothes although they were well-worn. So, taking the knight to be the captain, the young man addressed him, greeting him. Thereupon del Cano, in his grand manner, made a bow and would have led him to Carvalho, but the jealousy of the rough fellow woke and he stepped forward, in front of the knight and between him and the young man.

" I am the captain," said Carvalho. " This man is a nobody."

The knight's face grew very red with anger, but he made no trouble.

" My fault was no great one," said the young man, " because he has the face and bearing of a good man."

" I am a rough sailor and honest," said Carvalho. " You may trust me to be your host, and that in spite of my clothes. The man who works must needs look hard. The man who does nothing often looks well."

The young man smiled, but most of the smile went to del Cano. " I am your guest," he said to Carvalho.

He added, " My father is the King of Luzon and I carry presents to him from a chief. I am sure they will be safe in the junk."

" A luckless word," said Sebastian del Cano to Osberne. " Give the devil a finger and he'll take a whole hand."

So Carvalho led the way to the cabin and there the two stayed while the *Victoria* drifted with the slow wind, and the junk with it, being tied. Meanwhile some of the men on the junk came on to the ship, but a few stayed with the junk. Also some of the sailors made bold to get into the junk, where they handled and admired the rich fittings.

Almost an hour passed, and the natives had begun to wonder at the long visit of their prince, when there came on deck ten men-at-arms led by Martin of Genoa, all of them with pikes.

" Now I deem this means treachery," said del Cano to Osberne, and the words had barely passed his lips when up came Carvalho, and behind him the prince, who, though bound with ropes and stripped of his silken clothes, still carried his head high.

Then burst forth like a madman Carvalho. He shouted, " It is the fortune of war. Your prince is my prisoner and he dies if you do not ransom him with all that you have."

" Now by all the saints I am a faint heart if I let this pass," said del Cano. Whereupon he leaped at a man-at-arms, and, holding him with his left arm, pulled the sword with which the man was armed from its sheath. Before any could move, the knight ran across the deck and had the point of his sword at Carvalho's throat. " Now yield thee, dog and liar! " he cried. " This is the end of your mischief, as I live."

Down went Carvalho on his knees, white and shaking. Once he opened his mouth to shout something, but the point of del Cano's sword was pricking his throat.

"Ha! swine. So you like not the medicine," said del Cano, and pricked again. At that Carvalho threw himself flat on the deck, face downwards.

"Mercy! Mercy! I yield," he said. "Kill me not!"

"Now hear me, one and all!" said del Cano, full of fire. "Is this ruin to go on? I ask you now. Are you content to go as we have gone?"

"Not I," shouted one.

"Nor I," said another, "for we are heartily sick of it all."

Then Martin of Genoa, who commanded the men-at-arms, stood forth from the rest, after signing his men to make no move. "I and my men are with you, Sebastian del Cano, if you will proclaim yourself captain. We will work gladly for a man we can trust. Do I speak your minds, men?"

"We are with you," one of them said.

"Hear, all of you!" cried Sebastian del Cano. "If you are with me I shall make order out of disorder. If you are not, then I shall go with these in the junk and leave you to what may befall. This dog of a pirate knows nothing. He comes to me for his navigation. Without my knowledge the ships are lost."

Then Miguel de Rodas, quartermaster of the ship, spoke. "Captain Sebastian del Cano," he said, "we have long wanted a leader. Be you our leader. We are no pirates, but honest men. Guide us. Command us. My sword and my body are at your service."

"Osberne of Portsdown," ordered del Cano, "take the bonds from this prince. Clothe him. Honor him as best you may.

And you, Gubileto, tell him that I dare not leave the deck, but make it clear to him that I am ashamed because of the treatment he has received."

Then del Cano went to where the prince stood, and bowed low in most gracious manner. And he, so lately hopeless of escape, now understanding something of how things were moving, made a sign of friendliness. So that miserable affair came to an end and the present junk sailed away again. And all that day the men went to work with a good heart, cleaning the ship and making everything orderly. Also the *Victoria* drew close to the *Trinidad,* and when the two ships were near enough, Miguel de Rodas stood in the rigging and made announcement that they had chosen a new captain, and that Carvalho lay in chains below.

On the afternoon of a Friday, on the eighth day of November of the year fifteen hundred and twenty-one, the two ships sailed into Tidor the Beautiful, their flags aflutter and their bombards roaring, with the hearts of all men happy because at last they had found the Spice Islands. And never had that place seen such trading as began, for every one was friendly. A yard of ribbon was declared to be ample payment for a hundred pounds of cloves and spices, and it was cloves and spices that Europe needed, and would pay well for. Looking-glasses, beads, old iron, bent nails, trinkets, old clothes, broken knives, scissors that would not cut made for trade; all these were taken by the natives who brought down for sale to the ships, spices, cloves, rare woods, perfumes, fruits, gold, precious stones, birds of paradise, rugs. Not a sailor but bought enough to make him a rich man for life, and as for fair treatment, the order of Sebastian del Cano had gone forth that any seaman or officer or page who should as much as lay a rough hand upon a native would suffer punishment in sight of all. But Espinosa on the *Trinidad* far outdid all traders. He begrudged the space for the eighty barrels of water that they took on for the voyage to Spain. His own cabin was so crowded there was barely place for himself. The hold was jammed. The decks were piled.

" It is folly to load the hold without first seeing to the ship," said Poncero, a pilot and a cautious man, to Espinosa. " Spare a day to go over the ship and make ready for the voyage home."

" As good have no time at all as not make use of it," answered Espinosa. " We take a little risk to be sure, but our ship has sailed many a thousand miles and will sail a few thousand more."

" Swift risks often go before hasty falls," said the pilot. " I have seen wet places in the hold, and wet places mean weak timbers."

" The fool fears danger. A brave man faces it," said Espinosa. " Load the ship and get all that we can."

" Big mouthfuls choke," answered Poncero.

" Obey your orders and leave me to attend to the ship," said Espinosa, angrily. " I am captain and love my life as well as you love yours."

" As you will," said Poncero, and went about his business.

But the fears of the pilot were not idle. When the day came for sailing, the *Victoria* stood out of the bay and lay to at the mouth waiting for the *Trinidad* which could not clear as she should have done, because so hastily and carelessly had the cargo been taken on that the anchor chain had become fouled. But at last the *Trinidad* stood out to sea, not trim and upright like a good ship, but leaning, and somewhat down by the head. So the *Victoria* sailed in again, and when they were close enough they saw Hans standing in the rigging, and heard his loud voice.

"We have sprung a leak," he said.

"It is nothing much," shouted Espinosa. "A few hours will settle it."

"Not so," bawled Poncero. "There can be no sailing without unloading."

"It is a leak that can be patched from outside, if we run aground," came from Espinosa.

But soon all were persuaded that the ship must founder, so swiftly did the water come into the hold. They ran the *Trinidad* into a sand bank at half tide, and natives dived, and swam under water close to the hull, with their long hair loose, thinking that some great hole would be found into which their hair would be drawn.

"Saw man ever such folly?" said Poncero. "The leaks are a thousand and more. Every plank has its crack. There is nothing for it but to unload and lose what we have."

"Grieve not, Espinosa," said Sebastian del Cano. "Yet we must laugh to see how greed and grief run together in you."

"You laugh at my grief because of all that waste," answered Espinosa. "But when my grief is old yours will be new."

"We shall see! We shall see!" answered del Cano.

Nevertheless there was the cargo three parts spoiled, and the rest of it set out on the beach. It was plain that the *Trinidad* must be patched and calked if she were to sail again, and such a work would take weeks.

"This much is clear," said del Cano at a council. "We cannot stay and wait for the *Trinidad*. The *Victoria* must go on, and the *Trinidad* must follow when she is shipshape again."

"Think you that I would be a fool to go alone across seas

where Portuguese traders must fall on us and play pirate?"
said Espinosa. "The two ships together can take care of themselves. One sailing alone must be taken prisoner. Your *Victoria* will never get to Spain."

"Then what else would you do?" asked del Cano. "And
why should you who have played pirate be in so great fear
of pirates?"

"I have in mind the Panama neck where Balboa went,"
said Espinosa. "I talked with Balboa and heard how he stood
on a peak, from which he saw this very South Sea we have
sailed. Now across that neck of land a man may walk in a
day, and so be on the Spanish sea again. To that I would sail
and thus be all the while in Spanish waters. And it is my
idea that the *Victoria* should wait until we are ready, then sail
with us. That way lies safety. Your way, del Cano, lies
danger."

Sebastian del Cano said nothing for a time. He took the
copper ball on which the map of the world was engraved, that
which Behaim had made for Cristobal de Haro, and traced
out the course Espinosa favored.

"Almost due east you would sail," he said. "That needs
small knowledge of navigation." Then he thought awhile.

"It will not do for the *Victoria,*" he said. "I have set my
face on rounding the world, and shall do it. You may go as
you please. How many men do you want?"

"All told we are one hundred," said Poncero.

"Then we shall gather the men and draw lots, fifty to go
with the *Trinidad,* and fifty to go with the *Victoria,*" said del
Cano. "Does that please you?"

"It is a good way," answered Espinosa.

So that was done. The men gathered together and the page

Gubileto was chosen to tell them what had been said, then to have the men cast dice, the even numbers to go with the *Victoria* and the odd numbers to go with the *Trinidad*.

So the men drew together and the casting of the dice began. The page Gubileto called out names.

"Rodriguez the deaf throws nine and goes with the *Trinidad!*"

"A good companion, thank the saints," said Hans.

"Luis de Molino throws four and goes with the *Victoria*," chanted the page, and the man who had beheaded his own master at San Julian stepped across the line and took his place with the del Cano men.

"That is a fellow we could well spare," said Osberne.

Then Carvalho took the dice.

"It will be bad for whatever side wins him," said Hans.

"Carvalho throws four and goes with the *Victoria*," said the page. "Maestro Ance will throw."

"Now may my luck stay with me," said Hans, and threw. Out rolled one dice with a two and the other with a three.

"Ance the gunner must go with the *Trinidad*," called the page.

"Leon the Genoese with the *Trinidad*," he said again.

"Now comes my turn and I am divided, Hans," said Osberne. "I would be with you, but also I would be with del Cano."

So he threw the dice and they rolled out a six and a four."

"Osberne makes ten and sails with the *Victoria*," called out the page. So Hans and Osberne shook hands sadly.

"I wish that we could have gone together," said Hans, "but fate has spoken. Still we have been good companions."

"But we shall meet again, never fear," answered Osberne.

" And some day we shall sail in the same ship, I hope with Sir Robert of Portsdown, and with better company."

" It is something to hope for," answered Hans. " True the hope is small, but daylight will peep through a little hole, as they say in Germany."

So at last the men stood in two parties of fifty each, then farewells were said and the men sent to their appointed ships.

But in the morning, when the *Victoria* had stood out to sea, on a day of golden sunshine and pleasant wind, with the blue sea thick with racing white waves, and when the men were counted again, it was found that only forty-seven were aboard. And the names being called, none answered to the call of Luis de Molino, or of Carvalho, or of Ginez, for they had deserted to the *Trinidad*. So the *Victoria* anchored that evening at an island and Osberne with the page, Gubileto, went ashore.

The people, who were most pleasant and kind, asked many questions about the ships and their journey. So Gubileto told them of Spain, and of its towns, and its king, and its people, and when he had done the chief made a long talk.

" Now what do you think? " asked Gubileto of Osberne, when the chief had ended. " It does not surprise them what I have told them. They know almost as much as we know about Spain, it seems, and the chief says that there has been a man in these parts many years ago. Barthema was his name. This man came here with some Chinese traders and made friends with the people."

" And we thought ourselves to be the first," said Osberne. " Also we hoped to be the first in the straits, but there had been the de Haro ship before us. We looked to be the first to go round the world, but there was Enrique the slave who was first. And here we are where East touches West."

"The thing is that the chief tells me that some of his people would be willing to sail with us to Spain for adventure and profit's sake," said Gubileto. "They have long wanted to go, some of the boldest of their young men."

"It will please the captain," said Osberne. "The treachery after the throwing of the dice leaves us woefully short, and I have heard del Cano often say that because a man is dark-skinned he lacks nothing in manhood."

The end of it was that six young men, tall and straight and strong, presently came to Osberne and Gubileto, and began to talk and to tell how they were willing to work. They would go to the ship that moment and were ready. They also knew others who would go, and who were willing to start.

So Gubileto told them what they must expect in the way of wind and weather and cold, and perhaps hunger and thirst, but the tale did not change them. They were ready, they said, and showed that they were by saying farewell to the chief and their friends even while running down to the beach where a prau lay. "Go you with them," said Osberne, "and I shall come with the other six as soon as may be."

Thereupon Gubileto and the six, with a steersman, pushed the light prau into the sea and the wind caught the sail, and over the smooth water they went to where the *Victoria* lay outside the reef. And Osberne went up the beach, and up the hill slope to where several natives were making a new village, as it seemed. With him went two men who could tell the others what was Osberne's mission, both of whom said that they would go to Spain. And all fell out as had been told, for there were more than six who wished to go, for adventure's sake, besides the two with Osberne; so, with much laughter they settled among themselves upon six, putting blades of grass between leaves and choosing those who drew forth the longest grasses. But one of them pulled Osberne's sleeve and pointed to the sky which was blazing blue, though a haze seemed to be about the sun, like a cloud of yellow light. He said something in the manner of a man urging haste, and Osberne took it to mean that they must hasten because of a coming storm.

They lost no time, even went running down to the place where a prau lay in a small river that ran into the sea; but before they were there a noise of wind was high in the air, and the trees on the hilltop moved like sea-waves. Then came a sudden gloom, and the men with Osberne went quicker than before, not talking much but doing things with haste, pushing out the prau and raising the sail. And down came the wind, not where they were because it was a hill-sheltered place, but out in the bay and outside the reef, as Osberne saw, so that the *Victoria* began to pitch and strain, and the waves came rolling up, sweeping over the reef. Never had Osberne seen so sudden a change, nor had he believed that a storm could be so swiftly unchained, but it seemed to him, and he thought that it seemed to those with him, that they might reach the ship. The other prau had already gained the land, and natives were pulling it up the beach. But a new wind came rushing down the hillside so that their prau flew like magic, so swiftly that the white water curled high, and the mast strained, and the sail bellied as if it would break loose; and the cords whistled and were tight strung as fiddle strings. But a greater wind struck them, and the men leaped to their feet and held to ropes and mast to stay them, but quite without signs of fear. The air seemed full of grass and flying leaves, and of pieces of reed that stung when they struck a man's face. Yet the steersman stood, with his legs far apart, and his steering oar firmly held, driving the craft straight for the reef which showed in a white line. That second wind seemed to hit the *Victoria* crossways so that she heeled over. Osberne, watching sharply, thought she had foundered, but there were good seamen on board and everything was well done.

Before the prau had crossed the reef, and she could not turn back because of the fierce wind, the *Victoria* was flying before the storm without a sail set. So the prau plunged into the rough water outside of the reef, the plaything of fierce winds, while across the sky swept great dark clouds, and lower clouds seemed to whirl above the craft. Then day changed into night, though it was not much past noon and they saw nothing more of the island, or of the *Victoria,* but only mighty hills of gray-green water that rose high and sometimes curled over, so that it was as if they would fall upon and crush the little boat. But well she climbed the mountains of water, and well she slid down into depths to climb again; and without complaint the men on her did what they thought well to do, none saying anything, but each taking his turn at the steering oar. Yet at times in a boiling sea she strained as if she would go to pieces, and the lashings that held her together seemed to Osberne as if they must burst asunder. But all that day and all that night they could do nothing but run before the demon wind, and the night stretched out long and slow and terrible. When day came there was no sun, but only a cloud of light that rose on their left; and all that day the storm ran furiously, the sea white with flying spray; and a yellow gleam that was the sun climbed in the sky, while sometimes a wave broke that struck the prau so that she trembled. Nor had they bite or sup, yet no man said anything in complaint, so that Osberne, though he feared in his heart, still felt strong, and thought that all would fall out well somehow.

On the second night the black sky seemed to be torn asunder with a flare of white lightning, then thunder crashed, not in a sudden clap, but in a mighty roll that seemed as though it would never end. After that came rain so great that it beat down the waves; and the wind fell; and with their hands the men had to bail out the craft. So came the third day when the sun blazed in a clear sky and they went slowly, under a gentle wind and over a blue sea in the midst of which they were alone. Yet in spite of hunger and thirst no man said a word of his suffering, and the steersmen kept a straight course with the sun on their left hand in the morning and on the right at evening. Sometimes one of the men would point to the south and say the word "Sambawa" which puzzled Osberne very much, until one of them, seeing his puzzlement, made clear by making signs of eating. So Osberne took the word to be the name of a place to which they steered and felt comforted somewhat, though he wondered about the *Victoria*. As they sailed that day, all of them very hungry, Osberne began to see that they knew their goal. They were steering a course as a good navigator would, with no man among them making question. So he began to understand that they also knew the seas they sailed just as the men of Portsdown knew the English Channel and the Irish Sea, and he saw his own folly in thinking that all natives were ignorant. For if the men of Portsdown had parted from a ship by accident of storm in the Biscay Sea and that ship had been bound for Norway, then those who had been so parted being wishful to find their companions would steer for the Strait of Dover and so meet the lost ship. Therefore he must put his trust in these new courageous companions, holding that they would do their task in wise and proper fashion.

And so it turned out. Presently land came in sight like a dark blue cloud on the horizon, and the men pointed and said the word " Sambawa! " They smelt the sweet smell of the forest long before they saw the trees plainly. When they drew near the land there were men and women on the sea-beach, not at all eager or wondering, but looking as the people of Ports-down used to look at a ship newly come to port, ready to be friendly and ready to talk. On the beach like fairy boats lay canoes, and other canoes floated at anchor. Soft wind, and dark blue sea, kindly people, and fluttering birds and butter-flies, cool water and clean food, all these made it like a dream to Osberne after the hungry days of storm. It seemed strange to him that before the cool of evening, when a breeze came across the bay fanning him to sleep, he and his companions were well rested and refreshed and ready to work again. But much he wished that he knew the language and could talk to people. His heart felt heavy too when he remembered that had the fleet sailed into such a place as this, with a rascally captain at the head to command as he chose, then there would have been death and destruction, and evil matters afoot.

When morning came Osberne was awakened by one of the men of the prau who made him understand that they were about to sail again. At first Osberne felt sorry to know that, for to rest awhile and to wait for the *Victoria,* if indeed it would come that way when the world was so wide, and there were so many ways to go among all those islands — that seemed good. But the man made a picture in the sea-sand with his finger by which Osberne knew that they would sail a circle to find the *Victoria*. When he went down to the prau he found it well laden with jars of water and with fruit.

So they sailed again, and on the second evening, when the setting sun made a golden lane along the sea, and when the sky had turned crimson, they saw against the northern horizon the brown-white sails of the *Victoria,* but because of the light wind the ship did not move. But the feather-light prau flew over the water, and before the stars were out had run alongside the ship.

"Hail, good fellows!" cried out Osberne, and would have shouted much more in his delight had he not seen that the men on the prau made no fuss at all, but only raised their hands as men might who looked to meet their fellows without thought of not meeting them.

"Hail, Osberne!" shouted Gubileto, a little ashamed of making much to-do, because the six natives on board made so little noise.

"You seem to have bettered me at navigation," said Sebastian del Cano, looking over the side, and talking in his quiet way.

"These did all, and I sat like a bale of stuff," said Osberne. "They know these seas. They have faith and constancy. Even in the storm there was no speck of fear in them."

So that was all the greeting, though at sea Osberne had dreamed of great doings, and of men flinging their arms about other men's necks, and a mighty hullabaloo of talk as had been the case when the ships of the fleet met in the straits. But when Sebastian del Cano called Osberne and heard his story, and learned how, many years before, the man named Barthema had been in that place and among those islands he nodded his head.

" I remember," he said. " A man from Bologna it was, who did marvelous things in journeying and at last saved the Portuguese fleet at Cananor by telling them of the Moors and how they were ready to attack. It was hearing his tale that stirred Magellan, who was then in the Portuguese service in India. But how are these people in the island you found? Tell me that."

So Osberne told of their friendliness, and of the safety of the harbor, which tale ran the same as that told by the six islanders on the *Victoria,* and because of which the ship's course had been steered that way.

That word of friendliness on the island passed about among the men, and they told one another that they would carry themselves well to deserve it, which they did, so that not only were the natives willing to help them repair and to calk the ship, which had been sadly strained in the storm, but they brought down food, and water too, and also sandal-wood and wax, giving all free. So when the *Victoria* sailed again, with the long journey across the Indian Ocean to Africa ahead, the men were in good spirits. And in that voyage they knew storm, and thirst, and hunger too, for before they came to Africa they had little but rice to eat, yet they were in good spirits, all of them. There were times when they knew the terror of hurricanes and of cyclones, and sudden storms of terrible wind, but they met all with brave hearts and clear minds because of courageous shouldering of burdens, and because of their trust in their leader. Many a good man died too, some of sickness, some being drowned when the fore-topmast carried away in a storm, and one falling overboard. At last they came to the Cape Verde Islands and there the captain sent Osberne to shore, with thirteen men, to buy rice and food.

"Now Osberne," said the captain, "keep a close watch on the men and let it not be known from whence we came. These are Portuguese and full of jealousy against all Spaniards. Give out that you come from America and all may go well. That indeed is true, though we have come by a roundabout way, and it was not the America of Columbus."

So Osberne, being in charge of the boat, steered to the shore. Then his mastery failed. For down came white men. There were soldiers, citizens, bakers, wine-sellers, children, dogs, all of which none of them had seen for nigh on three years. And it was good to hear homely tongues once more.

"Ho, ye!" called one. "Come up to the town and tell us what news."

"What wares to sell have ye?" asked another.

"If ye come to buy, let me sell," said another.

And above the beach were houses, and a church, and more people. The sea-worn sailors heard the barking of dogs, the ringing of bells, the laughter of men, and crowing of cocks. For nigh on three years they had heard none of those sounds. They saw oxen yoked to carts, and wine-sellers going about with their wares, and laughing youngsters, and mules and horses. For nigh on three years they had seen none of those sights. Two ships were in the harbor, and boats were coming and going, and sea-gulls screamed, and good folk offered them friendship, and quiet men were making a business of living. But for almost three years such things had been to them like a dream half forgot.

"Mark you how good it is to see the blue smoke rising from a chimney," said Robert of Normandy, to Pedro of Tenerife.

"I have money in my pocket that I have carried around the

world and I must spend it," said Roldan the bombardier of the old *Concepcion*.

"And to buy what?" asked Alonso.

"The first thing that I see, whatever it may be," the gunner answered.

"I shall buy a crowing cock to remind me that I go no more to sea," said Mendez of Seville.

"And I, who bought a rat to eat on the Pacific, shall buy a piece of cheese," cried Felipe de Rodas.

"New bread for me," said Gasco of Bordeaux. "Bread with a crust of gold, and all white inside. I would give a piece of gold for it."

"And you, Osberne? What do you do?" asked Alonso.

"Look at the man! What does he see?" cried the page Juan. "Are you struck dumb, Osberne?"

"Not dumb," said Osberne. "But as I live, if I know a ship, there is the *Seagull,* Sir Robert's ship."

He pointed to a clean white ship with two masts, that lay in the bay. "Now you, Roldan, are in charge of the men. I am in charge of the boat. As I live I go not on shore just now but instead to my old ship, to see my old master."

"You are mad," said Roldan. "How shall you get there?"

"I shall swim," answered Osberne. "Go to shore all of you who wish, but for me my own people and my old companions. I could not be glad to be here with those who are part of my life there. It is ill to leave you, but I must do so."

"But why do that?" asked Roldan. "The boat may be ashore. Or the *Seagull* may have been sold," went on Roldan. "Strange things happen at sea."

"Then let us go to the town and see and hear," said Osberne, and when the boat touched the shore he was first to jump out.

So to the town they went, the seamen laughing and singing, the townspeople going with them, everybody talking and none listening. But before they entered the town, Roldan the gunner lifted his hand.

"Hear me," he commanded. "There is much to do, and Mendez and I have much to buy. Within two hours I shall blow my whistle, then let every man be on the beach near to the boat. Is it agreed?"

They gave a murmur, agreeing, then scattered this way and that, some to see things, some to talk, some to the wine-shop, some to the market place, but wherever a man went, there townspeople gathered about him, questioning him. And so well did Roldan and Mendez do their work, in spite of temptation, that one boatload of provisions went to the *Victoria*. It was a townsboat pulled by townsmen.

But something came to pass that changed everything, and it was this. In a wine-shop Pedro and Gomez and Alonso made very merry, and, somewhat light-headed, what with his joy at being among people of his own sort, and with what he had eaten and drunk, Pedro brought down his fist on the table and cried out, "Here are friends of mine, and here are people I do not know. But all are good people. The whole world is good. Even those who have been my enemies are good. Bring us then bread and cheese and wine and milk, and other things too for any who would eat and drink, friend or stranger."

"Who is to pay the reckoning?" asked the man of the wine-shop.

"I," cried Pedro.

"But you have spent your last coin, you said," said the host.

"Look you! I have enough to pay for a feast for the whole town," cried Pedro.

"Now put a bridle on your tongue, shipmate," said Gomez. "It will not do. After all, remember that these good people are of Portugal and not of Spain, and kings have been quarreling."

As he spoke there came in two men, officers of the town, who stood apart, listening and watching.

"See this," cried Pedro. As he spoke he took a bag from his shirt and emptied out cloves and spices on the table. "These are mine own," he cried. "I bought them in the Spiceries. I am a rich man. We have been round the world and found a country richer than all Portugal, richer than the country Columbus found."

"Now by my life, this is a matter for the King of Portugal," said the official. "Friends, I must arrest you in the king's name."

"An arrest!" shouted Gomez. "We have done nothing."

"You have done too much," said the official. "You have trespassed on the domain of the King of Portugal, who is the rightful owner of all eastern lands."

Then the man who was with the official put a trumpet to his mouth and blew a loud blast, and soldiers came running. And before an hour had gone, every one of the thirteen had been caught and were in prison. More than that, the official, with men and officers, put out to sea to take the *Victoria,* but Sebastian del Cano, scenting something to be wrong, had not dropped his anchor. So up went his sails as the boat came alongside, and an official, in a scarlet cloak, called out:

"Yield thee, in the name of his Sacred Majesty, the King of Portugal!"

"Come thou and take us," cried Sebastian del Cano, and the wind caught the sails and the white water swelled at the

Victoria's black bows. So, with eighteen men and four natives, the *Victoria* sailed out of the port at Cape Verde and on the eighth day of September, of the year fifteen hundred and twenty-two, sailed into the port of Seville. And it lacked twelve days of three years since they had started to go around the world.

But in the Cape Verde Islands the thirteen were in prison, though Osberne was not with them.

CHAPTER XIII

How Hans Escaped

OSBERNE, going about from place to place in the town
to learn something of the *Seagull,* heard the hue and
cry. For a short while he was troubled in his mind.
"Now," he asked himself, "is this another of those worries
that always come when our men land? After all, no one gets
into trouble without his own help, and I am all for peace. So
I shall let things be." Thereupon he skirted about the town
and made for the sea-beach, not near the *Victoria's* boat but
to the east and beyond a point that ran out into the bay, from

which, as he judged, he could not be seen from the town but could see both the *Seagull* and the *Victoria*. To get to the beach at that place he must needs go into a narrow valley, then cross a mountain stream which ran crookedly, then mount a low hill, all of which he did. Being at the top of the rise he stopped and laughed aloud. For on a patch of green by the mouth of the stream five white tents were pitched, and two boats lay on the beach, boats which by the shape and painting he knew to be of Portsdown make. They carried the red stripe from bow to stern without which no Portsdown boat ever entered water. And there were men sitting in the boats, and some were rolling casks of water from the brook, and others not on watch but playing, and many of them shouting and laughing. For three of the sailors bestrode asses and were trying to urge them to a race, the men all the time rough in what they said. But the silly talk came to Osberne like sweet music.

" With four legs can you go no better than that? " he heard one man say to the ass he rode, for the animal would not budge.

" The beast shows that not all asses have four legs," shouted another sailor, and laughed loud at his own poor joke.

" Nor have all asses long ears," roared the rider.

" And some two-legged asses bray louder than those with four legs," answered the other.

So others joined in, saying merry things, and silly.

" Sorry jokes they are," said Osberne to himself, " but good to hear all the same," and found himself minded to go running down the hill and proclaim himself. Then it came to him that it would be a fine thing to pretend himself to be foreign born and somehow get onto the ship and presently surprise himself and his shipmates too. So he checked his pace and went more soberly, feeling that he might pass as Portuguese the easier because there were islanders sitting a little apart, those who owned the asses, as he judged. But when he drew nearer to his fellow countrymen his heart began to thump and he found himself not quite so willing to play the part he had set himself to play. However, he drew near to one young fellow who had a ruddy face and a close curling beard, for him he knew to be the brother of Hugh of the Mill, though he had been beardless when Osberne knew him at Portsdown. When he greeted the lad in Spanish, still playing his part, Hugh's brother looked at him as he might have looked at a would-be friendly dog, then answered, loudly and as if talking to a deaf man, that being the English way with foreigners, " No savvy. Ask some other. Me no talk your way. Savvy?" Then he nodded several times, and, as Osberne thought, seemed somewhat sorry for all the world of men that spoke no English. Next he turned to a big man, one freckled and red-headed, and very broad of chest, and said, "Ho! Bob. You know something of the French. Here is a foreign man who wants something."

The man called Bob turned, grinning, and asked, " *Que voulez vous, hombre,*" mixing tongues, Spanish and French, carelessly.

Hearing that, Osberne tried to look serious, though his heart bade him take the man's hand and shake it, or slap the fellow on the back, or shout aloud, until Bob said, " But, stranger, look merry at least."

Then the mate came up and said, " The fellow looks like a seaman, in spite of his clothes. We could trim him into shape by the time we got to Portsdown."

So Osberne opened his mouth to say the speech he had

OSBERNE of PORTSDOWN

prepared, pretending to be foreign, but instead, out came this, "How is Portsdown? How is Sir Robert? How is Hugh of the Mill, and Rob the tanner, and Jack's dog Watchet, and Will Long, and old mother Tipton who makes the marmalade, and Tom the farrier, and Bob who keeps the King's Head Inn? And tell me about —"

Then Hugh's brother looked in Osberne's face and cried, "Why I say it is Osberne himself. Look! There is the scar he got playing quarterstaff with Tom the tanner. I would know him anywhere."

"Here, Harry," shouted the mate to one of the men at the brook. "Look you here! Here is the same Osberne that used to live at Portsdown." And the man called Harry came, not running, but going heavily as was his way.

"Osberne," he said sheepishly, as he shook hands, not with any show of joy but as if he had parted from him only the day before.

Others came, some to slap him on the back, some only to look, saying nothing, some to grin, some to ask questions that found no answer just then. But it all wore off in short time, and the mate said, gruffly, "To work, lads! We cannot stand here gaping. You talk like a crowd of old women. Get the water down to the beach. Look after the lashings. You, Osberne, can pull an oar."

So those who had gathered about the newcomer went to their work and before an hour had gone in working Osberne was as an old tale, and much as if he had been shipmate among them with no three year's absence.

But happy was Osberne's heart when he came alongside the *Seagull,* so happy that he must needs put out his hand secretly and touch the black hull. And how the years fell away from

him when he set foot on the deck and saw the old things, the
ship's bell, the cabin door with a scar on it, the white deck
with a scooped place made by a cannon ball, the ropes neatly
coiled, the wrinkled-faced cook who grumbled saying, "Another hungry belly to fill." And while Osberne stood gaping
at everything, he heard his name called, so turned to see Sir
Robert, then doffed his cap. So Osberne's heart must needs
leap again to see the knight, his face brown with sun and
wind, his eyes like a hawk's, his body strong and square-
shouldered.

"How now! What is all this?" asked the knight.

"A lucky day for me, sir," answered Osberne.

"So you have been around the world, and the first man to
do so," said the knight. "There must be a strange tale to tell."

"Not the first man, sir. A slave was the first."

"Well, we shall hear the story later," said the knight.
"There are things to do. But first get into clothes that become a seaman." Then the knight went about the deck in his
own old way, looking at this and at that, finding something
to do here and something else there for the men, nor did he
see Osberne again until near sunset, when he heard a part of
his tale, not told in any straight fashion, but a piece here and
another there. And when Osberne came to the story of how
thirteen of the *Victoria's* men lay in prison after going around
the world, the knight looked serious.

"Why, what in the name of all the saints should it mean
to keep men in prison for a handful of cloves and stuff? Out
upon such villainy, say I! I had a mind to row out to this
Victoria, seeing how sea-worn she looked. And I wondered
what had gone wrong when she sailed away again with the
port's boat hailing her."

"How long, think you, must the men stay in prison?" asked Osberne.

"It shall be a poor matter if they sail not with me to Spain tomorrow," answered the knight.

"I trust without bloodshed," said Osberne. "I am sick of fighting and death."

"As to that, words are better than arrows, and sometimes gold is better than speech," answered the knight. "I have brought a cargo to this place and know the captain of the port as a good man. Most men are good when hate has not been drilled into them. But we shall see. We shall see. And you may dress yourself well and come ashore as my serving-man. You have grown too big to play the page."

As they walked the street of the town, two hours later, they met the captain of the port himself walking in front of his own house.

"Why, I was sending to ask you to come," he said, in fair English. "I would that you had been here earlier."

"What has passed?" asked Sir Robert.

"This. I have thirteen men in prison, who are doubtless smugglers. One of them offered cloves and spices for sale, and from whence should they come but from Portuguese lands I ask?"

"From the Spiceries, most certainly," said Sir Robert.

"From the Spiceries," echoed the captain of the port. "And what think you that they said?"

"How should I guess?" asked Sir Robert in reply.

"They said that they had gained the Spiceries by going round the world to the west and sailing on until they came to the Islands," answered the captain of the port, and laughed aloud at what he deemed the folly of it. "Said I, 'Be silent or speak something worth hearing.' But still they protested that they spoke truth. My very clerk laughed aloud in the court. The jailers laughed. I had to hold my sides."

"Yet," said Sir Robert, "they spoke the truth."

"Sir Robert! What say you? Do I hear aright?"

"Why, it is true, Captain," said the knight. "This young man, my servant since a child, went with the ships and is returned as you see."

"Now," said the captain, "can it be that I have put in prison men who have made such a brave journey? Am I like the poor man who refused a cucumber because it was crooked? Am I a fool like him who bolted a door with a boiled carrot?"

"Not that, Captain," said Sir Robert. "But I know the tale to be true. You doubted, it is true, but doubt is the key of knowledge. Truth is a club that knocks down every one."

"But the world will hold me as a laughing-stock," said the captain. "You know how they say, 'A Portuguese apprentice who cannot sew but would be cutting out.'"

"There is another saying which runs, 'From the same flower a bee extracts honey but a wasp gall,'" said the knight. "It is in your power to do a gracious act, Captain."

"And what is that?"

"Loose these men. Send them to Spain after you have fed them and dressed them."

"But I have no ship, and none will be here until the fleet comes from Cochim."

"You have the Seagull, Captain. I shall gladly give the men passage. I owe you the service and much more that I cannot repay."

So the captain of the port took Sir Robert to the back of the garden while Osberne stood in waiting. And the two of them sat at a table and drank and ate, while, at a given order, messengers came and went. Presently a trumpeter called the people to the great cross in the market place, and a herald made a speech telling the people how men who had gone round the world should be honored. Then the captain of the port and Sir Robert with some men-at-arms made a fine show in marching to the market place. After that, Osberne, being sent, went to the jailer's house and there greeted Roldan and the rest, all of them in such clothes as could be found in the town, some of them new and some the worse for wear, none of them fitting very close. So, after a trumpet blast, they all marched to the market place, and the people shouted, and the bells pealed, and the dogs barked, and the captain of the port said that he greatly honored the thirteen for their bravery, and the men, so newly out of prison that they blinked at the light, wondered at the change in their fortunes.

"What does it all mean?" asked Hernando. "Can it be that we are at liberty to go to the place where we are to be killed, like a pig let out of his sty?"

"I would be glad if I were wise enough to understand," said Robert the carpenter.

"Mind not your wisdom," put in Roldan. "A drop of good luck is worth a cask of wisdom. It is a life of ups and downs. Time has been when I thought myself unluckier than a dog in church, and many's the time I have told myself that had I been born a maker of hats, then men would have been born without heads. So here at last is good luck and I am for shouting with the rest of them."

The others found themselves of Roldan's mind so they cheered and waved their caps as if they had been boys. Also they went to the church because other people were going that way, and when they were there the priest blessed them; then the innkeeper shouted that the captain of the port had ordered a feast to be set for the thirteen and it was all ready. None of them needing a second bidding they went to the inn, every man grinning at his fellow and saying that the day was a blessed one. And after the feast the thirteen went on board the *Seagull,* so there were many willing hands to clear the good ship for sea and for Spain. Two days out, what with a clean ship, and good company, and healthy food, and sound sleep, it seemed to Sir Robert that the years fell from the men after they had bathed and shaved, and trimmed their hair. Said he, one day, when they were abreast of the Canaries, "I had thought that all of ye were near to being old men, what with dirt and wrinkles and old rags."

"Why, as to that," said Roldan, "a younger crew never sailed the sea, except perchance some fisher craft; but certainly not for a long voyage. There were many younger than Osberne here. There was Juan de Acurio in the *Victoria,* to this day he is barely twenty-eight. There was Rodriguez no more than twenty-two when we started, but looking much younger. And Martin. How old was Martin?"

"A boy just turned fifteen," said Hernandez. "I mind that I asked him if he had come with his mother."

"And there were two Juans," went on Roldan. "One of them was fourteen, the other sixteen. Rodriguez looked young, but his age was twenty-three. Come to think of it, Felipe here is about the oldest of us. How many years do you number?"

"Forty-seven and no more," answered Felipe. "It was a fleet of young men, and Magellan himself was no more than thirty-six when he died."

That same wonder at the youth of the fleet struck many a one at Seville, when the *Seagull* anchored and the thirteen met the eighteen with the *Victoria*. People wondered that there was no feebleness of body, or sadness of countenance, for all that they had suffered and adventured. Their muscles were like steel, and their skins clear. And as they walked in procession in the great show that was made to celebrate the return and the voyage, they laughed merrily in a wholesome way, and they jested with the bystanders, and they carried themselves in light-hearted fashion. So people called them the *Courageous Companions,* and hailed them.

At the king's pavilion, for the king had to sit in state and see them, they stood upright in the midst of the grandees, and they bowed when told to do so, but very unhandily.

The king sat on a gilded chair, and all about him stood men with banners. He wore his crown, and his clothes were hemmed with pearls and rubies. Also gold and pearls and gems shone and glittered on the lords and ladies who stood near.

"A king's a king and must hang himself with baubles," whispered Hernando to his fellow. "These are not any whit different from the rajahs we saw."

"But look at Sebastian del Cano," whispered back Juan. "There is a man, every inch of him. It is well that the king sits, else our leader would overtop him, and outshine him as he did outshine Carvalho."

When the trumpeter blew a fanfare the gentlemen and knights took their swords from their sheaths and held them high, so that they glittered in the sun. Then other nobles came, some from the right and some from the left, grouping themselves according to their rank in a half-circle with the king in the middle of it; and some were in shining helms and armor, others in cloaks and dresses and doublets of crimson, and blue, and purple, and snow-white, and canary-yellow, and ebony-black according as their family custom went. And such was the rustling noise they made, because while they were crowded many a one wanted to stand forth to be seen, placing an elbow on a hip to look big and square, or placing his cloak so that the fineness of it might show, or wriggling more to the front to be seen — such was the rustling noise that when a man dressed in blue silk read from a scroll, no one heard his words, nor seemed much to care. When he had done ten trumpeters blew a blast, after which another man with a voice that cracked sadly read something from another scroll and all that could be well heard was in praise of the king and his generosity. Then a third man read from a third scroll, beginning bravely enough with, " Shipmates and friends," but soon fell to testifying to the greatness of the king, who, as it seemed, had spent the three years in sleeplessness because of his care for the fleet.

" Mark you how he called us shipmates and friends," said Robert from behind his hand to Osberne. " And all his sailing, I'll warrant, has been done on the swan pond with the ladies, and a page rowing the boat."

" Saw you his white hands? " whispered Roldan. " I would as lief try to make an arrow out of a pig's tail as a sailor out of the man."

" Surely," whispered Osberne, " this king must be all abashed hearing that praise."

" Hold your tongue," said Juan. " He likes it. Flattery is a sweet food for those who can swallow it. He hath an appetite for that sort of thing, like all kings."

When another trumpet rang out two of the king's pages,

very bravely dressed in purple and green silk, made signs beckoning the sailors to the king's closer presence. They led the men to where a carpet that moment had been laid over the finer carpet, lest rough shoes should sully its fineness, and there the two pages arranged the sailors, pushing and pulling them to make them stand in line. Then a man in a suit of cloth of gold read something, which, he told the king, was the speech of thanks made by the sailors, running over the first part of it very swiftly, but going slower when he came to the place where the king was praised. While he read, the seamen shifted from leg to leg, and coughed in their throats, and made noises, and sometimes scratched their heads, for they were tired and hot and thirsty.

When the reader had done, one of the pages addressed the sailors, saying, "Now you have made your speeches, so must do as I do, in mannerly way." Then he went down on one knee, as graceful as a maiden, and beckoned to the seamen to do the same. But they moved rustily, and with much elbowing and shoving, getting in one another's way, and all of them feeling very much ashamed, for they were fretting to be gone. And that being the end so far as they were concerned they were led out, all of them very glad and grateful to get to the fresh air again.

But concerning what went on thereafter was not known to them, for the king and his nobles held a great feast in their honor, while they, heartily glad to be out of the grand company, found their way to the inn, where they ate bread and cheese and talked tremendously, laughed hugely, too, remembering the figure they had cut at the meeting. But there were real speeches, and kindness, and honor when Sir Robert and Osberne and the men of the *Seagull* said farewell to the

Victoria, though that was not until the day after the cargo was sold and the money shared.

It was Pigafetta who told Sir Robert about the vast sum of money the cargo sold for. " Some seven million and eight hundred odd maradevis," he said. " That is to say nothing of cinnamon and mace and nutmeg and sandal-wood and some gold. And there is this as the share and wage of your bold lad, Osberne." So saying he handed the English knight a bag of gold. "I say no more than that the lad put his shoulder under the load," Pigafetta added. "And so did many others. And many a good man did not come back with us. We must not forget those who struggled on to their end."

That saying took Osberne's mind back to his friends in Patagonia, to Ato, and the few he had lived with, and the fine free life he had known. That thought stayed with him somehow, the while he said his farewells to his shipmates of the *Victoria,* so that when he awoke in the morning of the day after, as the *Seagull* was running northward before a brisk wind along the Spanish coast, it seemed to him that he had said good-bye to the Patagonians but a few hours before. It seemed, too, when he saw Portsdown again, that the three years must have passed with lightning swiftness. The cruelty and coarseness had shrunk to a thin edge in his memory. The true and real part of it all lay in the companionship he had known. What was more, and that he could not quite under-stand, he found himself not very willing to talk about his adventures, and more than willing to hear the tales of quiet lives that the villagers had lived.

But, TRY as he would, Osberne could not bring himself to be content on shore. So he must needs sail on the *Seagull* wheresoever it went, for Sir Robert made him mate, and in time captain. Thus he saw Iceland, and Norway, and Ireland. And thus he also saw Portugal, and about that there hung a strange thing, which was this.

Being in Lisbon, and walking in the market place, there came to him a blind man, a beggar, who asked alms. When Osberne had given him a coin, the man said, " Sir. Tell me another thing. Not more than two hours ago, as I stood by the fruit stall, I heard men talking as they passed. They spoke of three prisoners who had been brought from Cochim, and I gathered that they had been round the world and were with this Magellan long ago. Can you tell me aught of them? "

" Now I have heard nothing," said Osberne. " Know you their names? ".

" All that I know is one was a captain, but the name of him has gone from my mind," said the blind man.

" Would it be Gonzalo Gomez de Espinosa? " asked Osberne.

" The very same," said the blind man.

" Would you remember the names of the others if I named names? " asked Osberne again, full of eagerness, but the blind man shook his head.

" Can you guide me to the prison then? " asked Osberne.

" That I can do well enough, for often I have been in it," was the answer.

So Osberne took the blind man's arm to guard him against dogs and stones and corners, and, thus protected, the beggar went forward at a lively pace, until they came to the common prison where Osberne gave his guide a coin and sent him on his way. Next, Osberne sought the jailer, whom he found sitting in the shade at the door, with a tankard in his hand.

He was a gross man, red of face, red of hair, red of beard; and he wore a dagger, and hanging to his belt was a bunch of keys.

" Friend — " began Osberne, when the jailer looked up and laughed.

" None call me that except there is something they want," said the jailer. " So come to your question, the sooner if there be money to make music."

" Fair enough," said Osberne, and laid down a coin. " There shall be other pieces go with that if all falls out well," he added.

" Money is a language that all men understand," said the jailer, as he picked up the piece and put it in his pocket.

" Tell me the names of the three sailor prisoners that have come from Cochim," said Osberne.

" Tell me how many gold pieces you have to spend," said the jailer.

" One name, one gold piece," answered Osberne. " And let me say you seem to be an open rascal."

" Rascal I am," answered the jailer, " else I would not be in this employ. A rascal without money is a bow without an arrow. Down with your coin for the first name, and, master, I warrant I tell you all the names, leaving the one you want until the last. For I know your speech to be that of an Englishman, so guess what you want."

Osberne put a gold coin on the table. " The first name then."

" Gonzalo Gomez de Espinosa, and a fellow not worth the coin you pay for his name," answered the jailer.

" The second," said Osberne, and put another coin in the fellow's hand. He added, " The name was hardly worth the price paid. But let it go. What next? "

" Gines de Mafra, a seaman," answered the jailer.

" The third," said Osberne, laying down another gold piece.

" A foreigner named Maestre Ance," answered the jailer. " It is the man you want."

" I would see him," said Osberne. " How much will it cost? "

" Belike your life," answered the jailer. " There is the jail fever busy, and men die. One man in the prison is so sick that he may not live through the night, and these men are in the common room."

" But I must see the man. Can you bring him out if I pay for the trouble? " asked Osberne. " Now be a good fellow. This man is dear to me."

" Who knows what might be," said the rascal jailer. " Bribes throw dust into men's eyes."

" Put forth thy hand," said Osberne.

The jailer laid an open hand on the table, and Osberne put three gold coins on the dirty palm.

" God send you more wit and me more money," said the fellow. " You might have seen the man for one coin." Having said that he rose to his feet and led the way to another side of the prison and there, in an outside cell, strongly barred, sat Hans himself, for in that place men were put each day to beg for the other prisoners.

" Said I not so? " said the jailer, but neither Osberne nor Hans took any notice of the rascal, for they were overjoyed to see each other's faces, and clasped hands through the bars as though they would never let loose. And all the while each plied the other with questions. Yet that sight was so common, that passers-by took no notice of it. Only Osberne turned to a gaping lad and gave him money, bidding him run and bring food for the prisoner. Soon the boy came back, and then Osberne and Hans ate together, Osberne doing so for the companionship of it, for he had no appetite at all, seeing his shipmate in that plight. And almost he wept for very rage when he thought of the cruelty of it all, for Hans had done nothing ill to deserve that punishment.

At length the jailer told them that it was time for them to part because Hans must give way to another begging prisoner, each taking his turn.

"But how if one prisoner is a better money gatherer than another?" asked Hans.

"That changes the case," answered the rascal jailer. "The guards get one-half of that which is collected, and a few maravedis at the most come to us."

"Then here is your share for the day, and another for the prisoners," said Osberne, as he put a gold coin into the box, and gave the jailer another. "It may be that after a little we shall see more."

"Let it be, then," said the rascal. "He that shows his money shows his judgment. Talk on. Besides, the prisoner whose turn it was died this morning."

So Hans began to tell about how, after the *Victoria* had left the *Trinidad,* Espinosa built a trading place on the island, and put Luis del Molino in charge over five men, and it was the same Molino who had cut off his own master's head at San Julian. He told how Carvalho died of the fever; how the *Trinidad* at last sailed for Panama; how they steered northeast instead of east because Espinosa knew nothing of navigation; how at an island three of the men deserted; how the food ran short and they were at last eating nothing but rice; how they ran into a storm that lasted five days which took away their mainmast and ruined their forecastle.

As Hans told his tale the jailer listened with open mouth, and with eyes set and straining. When the sailor came to the part telling about their hunger the jailer shook his head and said, "Poor soul! Poor soul! Indeed it is woeful."

"But what of the pilot Poncero?" asked Osberne.

"Espinosa would not listen to him," said Hans. "We got to latitude forty-three, then Espinosa turned back. Poncero thought we might the easier find land if we kept on."

"Now God help the fool!" said the jailer. "As I live, your Espinosa shall have dry bread for a week."

Hans went on with his story, telling how they went back to Tidor, and how the journey lasted six weeks, with thirty of the crew, counting some natives, having died, and the rest so weak that they could not do any work about the ship.

"So great a fool as this Espinosa I never saw," put in the jailer. "He is like the fool that would buy an ox to have cream. The first chapter of a fool is to think himself wise. He came to the jail telling me of his greatness, and since, he has been telling me my business every minute. But go on with the tale, Maestre Ance. Never heard I a more heart-breaking one. It seems that the Admiral De Brito made you prisoners as I have heard. What of that?"

"That is true," Hans went on. "De Brito, a Portuguese admiral, was in the islands with seven ships, and he found the storehouse and took all. Then he took the *Trinidad* too, and the nineteen of us who were left. Then he sent us prisoners to Malacca where we worked under the whip, building houses, Espinosa working like the rest until he told a tale of being admiral, whereupon he was allowed to sit in prison, doing nothing, while we toiled in the hot sun."

"Poor soul! Poor soul!" said the jailer. "But be of good

cheer. You shall have good food while I guard you. Trust me for that."

Hans went on to tell how they had been put into two junks and sent to Cochim, and how the boat in which Molino and Sanchez and Cota were went down in a storm.

"Now see that," said the jailer. "It was for a purpose. You were saved that you might meet this good gentleman."

"It may be," said Osberne, "that he was saved that you might have some kind hand in the matter."

"Now I had not thought of that," said the jailer. "But what can I do?"

"That is to be seen," said Osberne. "It may be that you are to provide for the safety of your soul by doing good works."

"But tell the tale, good Ance," said the jailer. "My eyes are keen and see how you have suffered."

"The rest is a weary history," went on Hans. He told how two managed to escape and got away on a ship, and how the rest of them were kept at Cochim; how so many died; how another escaped, until at last none were left except the three then in prison where they were cast after being taken in chains from Cochim. "But there is also Marfa," he said. "He too was a prisoner on the ship, but kept apart, because maps and books were found which he had hidden."

"Now my heart is well-nigh broke with this tale," said the jailer, and, indeed, tears were running down his cheeks. "Believe me, I have more heart than head."

"A good heart breaks bad fortune," said Osberne. "The saints may have chosen you to do something. Already you have done much."

"There is naught that I can do, alas!" said the jailer. "Here is the jail door and no one goes out of it alive. By the underground passage they go to the trial and I see them no more. But out of my door no living man passes, but only in."

"Now good man, hear me," said Osberne. "This is my friend and shipmate. You see how he has suffered. Look the other way and let me open the door. I shall give you gold enough to count to keep you busy. You shall add profit to a good deed."

"It will not do, my lord," said the jailer. "There is a to-morrow and a next day. These may be here for months, but when the name is called and I can give up no Hans, how then will it be for me?"

"Said you not, a little time ago, that there was one man dead in the prison?" asked Osberne.

"Yes, poor soul. A most happy release. He hath been here so long that I think him forgotten," said the jailer.

"Then hark ye! Why not call him Hans?" asked Osberne.

"What will that do?" said the jailer. "You can call a dead man by any name. A dead man does not speak to deny."

"And the dead man will not deny the name of Hans," said Osberne. "Hear me. Make your report that it is Hans that is dead, and let my friend slip out as soon as it is dark. If you fear, then come with me on my ship to England. I shall give you passage, with work to do when you get there."

But the jailer shook his head. "No. That would not do. A lie begets ten others, and I must e'en be here to father them. Nor must I see your man get through the door. But you said something about counting gold. I could count fifty pieces of gold the while a man slipped through the door."

"Listen," said Osberne, and put his mouth close to the jailer's ear. "Count twice fifty pieces. Then look under a stone that I shall lay there and count ten more. And there is also this. In another hour it will be dusk. You and I shall count the hour together when the clock strikes at nine, and for every stroke of the bell a gold piece shall drop to the table if I hold the key in my hand. Then you may fall to your counting. Now what do you say?"

The jailer said nothing for a long time, but cast many a side glance at Osberne. When he spoke he said, "You are as a tree that shades me from the heat of the sun of poverty. And it would be a fool who would cut down the tree that shades him. Now say no more until the counting time comes. But I am of a mind that the dead man's name shall be Hans."

So when evening fell Hans went back to the common prison and sat close to the door, and Osberne and the jailer took care that neither should lose sight of the other. But near nine Osberne could not choose but groan when the jailer weakened a little, saying that he feared to play such a trick.

"Fear not if you have gold," said Osberne. "Sorrow if you have none. Count you this." And, when the first stroke of the bell sounded, he began to drop gold pieces as he had promised.

Thus was Hans released, and thus the jailer found himself with more gold than he had ever dreamed of seeing. For the man gave up the key, and Hans slipped through the narrow opening without any in the prison knowing of it. Nor did the world hold two happier men than Hans and Osberne when the *Seagull* dropped down the Tagus and headed for the open sea.

SO HERE IS THE END OF THE CHRONICLES
OF THE "COURAGEOUS COMPANIONS"
WRIT BY SCRIBE MESSIRE ~~~
· CHARLES J · FINGER · FOR WHICH ·
· CERTAIN EMBELLISHMENTS HAVE BEEN ·
ENGROSSED BY JAMES DAUGHERTY.
~ ÆND ADMIRABLY PUBLISHED
BY MESSIRES LONGMANS GREEN + CO.
Æ · D · 1 9 2 9 ·